CW00502930

SEASONS OF
SEX & INTIMACY

Seasons of
Sex & Intimacy

For a Husband and
Wife in Marriage

Emma Waring

First edition

This paperback edition published in 2018

 First published in Great Britain by
HULLO CREATIVE LTD.
www.hullocreative.com

Printed and bound in Great Britain.

Any case studies or individuals that have been given as examples are purely fictitious and relate to no specific client Emma has worked with in her clinical practice.

ISBN 978-0-9935366-7-0

This book is dedicated to
my husband Steve.

Thank you for all the wonderful times, of which there are many. But more so, thank you for your unshakeable commitment to working at our marriage when it feels like hard work. Your steadfastness has taught me so much about love, and continues to do so.

Emma Waring is a sex and relationship therapist, cardiac specialist nurse, and Christian. Her pioneering work combining her nursing and therapist role was recognised when she won the Nursing Times Rising Star award in 2004. In 2001 Emma set up the Male Cardiovascular Health Clinic, an internationally renowned clinic for treating male cardiac patients with erectile dysfunction. This was the first clinic of its kind and she presented this unique work nationally and internationally. In 2011 she set up a clinic in a private hospital in London, working with individuals and couples experiencing sexual and relationship difficulties. She regularly speaks to healthcare professionals and in churches on how couples can nurture lasting sexual enjoyment in their relationship, and how to manage common sexual difficulties which are rarely discussed.

Past Professional Positions:

Chair of South East Erectile Nurses Association (SEENA) (2001-2005)

Chair of the Erectile Dysfunction Working Group, Guy's & St Thomas' NHS Trust (2001-2005)

Member of the editorial board for the European Society for Sexual Medicine newsletter (2004)

Member of the advisory panel for the British Sexual Dysfunction Association (2002-2004)

Secretary to the British Society for Sexual Medicine (2010-2014)

Professional Membership:

Royal College of Nursing (RCN)

Nursing & Midwifery Council (NMC)

College of Sex and Relationship Therapists (COSRT)

British Society for Sexual Medicine (BSSM)

European Society for Sexual Medicine (ESSM)

United Kingdom Association for Transactional Analysis (UKATA)

National Counselling Society (NCS)

Commendations for Emma Waring and
Seasons of Sex and Intimacy

Sex between a husband and wife can be one of God's richest gifts but sadly can also be the source of problems. These can be deepened by the fact that our culture – strong on talking about sex but weak in understanding – says so much that is both unhelpful and ill-informed. It is therefore a real pleasure to welcome this wise and intimate book from someone who knows what she's talking about. Many people are going to be very grateful for this!

Revd Canon J. John, speaker and author

Talking about sex and sexual intimacy in marriage has for a long time been a very taboo and secretive topic. We love how Emma has (with incredible knowledge and kindness!) discussed and addressed these issues in this book. We are sure many people (like ourselves!) will find it very informative and helpful.

Martin Smith: singer-songwriter & Anna Smith: author - together the parents of six children

This book is long overdue, simply because there hasn't been anything like it to help in this vital area of life. Relevant, concise, practical, hopeful, helpful…I could go on. It should be required reading for every couple preparing for marriage, and could be a lifeline to those who've been together for years or decades. Highly recommended.

Jeff Lucas, author, speaker, broadcaster

Contrary to what you see in romantic movies, most people struggle with sexual intimacy. In this sensitive but frank resource, Emma Waring, as a professional sex therapist, helps answer the questions that Christians are often afraid to ask because of shame and embarrassment.

Revd Dr Trevor Morrow, former Moderator of the Presbyterian Church of Ireland

Christians believe God made us and therefore God invented sex. Which makes the reluctance most church leaders have to talk or teach about what makes good sex rather weird. I recommend all married couples and those preparing for marriage invest in Emma Waring's eminently sane and practical book. It should help husbands and wives better enjoy this glorious God-given gift.

John Buckeridge, Deputy CEO of Premier Christian Communications

At last! A robust and genuinely helpful book about sex from a Christian faith perspective, written with a balance of compassionate clinical experience, broad-based research and intelligent insight. Emma somehow manages to bring detailed, specific advice to her book, while leaving behind the "cringe" factor that so often accompanies that advice. Missing too are the judgment, embarrassment and head-on-one-side pastoral pity that prevent those who struggle from seeking help. This book is for everyone looking forward to, enjoying – but especially struggling with enjoyment of – sex in heterosexual relationships.

Wendy Bray, Anglican priest and writer

Every couple goes through challenges in their sexual intimacy at some stage in their life and knowing where to go to get good quality help can be difficult. Emma's many years of training and experience as a psychosexual therapist make that help easily accessible in this excellent book.

Maggie Ellis, former Christianity *magazine agony aunt and accredited psychosexual therapist*

Marital sex is a great gift from God when it's good, and anything from a disappointment to a disaster when it isn't. But in our sex-obsessed society, the shocking truth is that almost no practical wisdom and guidance is available. Emma Waring's brilliant book, clear, concise, thorough, readable, non-prescriptive, practical and professional, is totally liberating. It is an essential read for every couple, and possibly a revelation for many, because most experience some bewilderment in this potentially fraught area at some point. We need a handbook that, at every age and stage of our lives, will enable us to enjoy the gift of marriage to the full. My husband and I, as church leaders, wish this book had been available a long time ago.

Michele Guinness, author, pastor's wife and former Head of NHS Communications in Cumbria and Lancashire

This is such a sane book. In my work as a priest and in my capacity as a Vice-President of Relate in my area of NW London, I know how much couples need good, honest and straightforward advice about their emotional and sexual lives. This book does the job without fuss, in plain language, and is not coy. It's set in the context of lifelong faithful commitment in marriage – and will be helpful to Christians and those of all faiths and none. Really helpful stuff.

Pete Broadbent, Bishop of Willesden

Emma has helped many couples, using her vast professional and pastoral experience. Many people have experienced significant breakthrough in their relationships. We are delighted therefore that she has now made this knowledge and material accessible to a wider audience in the form of this book, so that more of us can benefit from her insights, wisdom and good sense.

Archie & Sam Coates, Senior Pastors, St Peter's Brighton

This book is packed full of really useful information about sex and sexual intimacy that Christians have, in the past, not wanted to talk about. It's also a book that offers invaluable help and guidance in a professional, yet accessible, way for all couples regardless of what season they are in or how long they've been together. We've no doubt that it will be a great resource and blessing to many many marriages.

Tim & Rachel Hughes, Lead Pastors / Gas Street Church, Birmingham

CONTENTS

From a couple who have worked with Emma Waring

We first went to see Emma because we had been married for a year and still hadn't been able to have sex. We were confused about what was wrong. We had grown up in environments where sex was talked about very little and knew nothing of the potential complications. The sessions with her have made such a difference to our lives. She talked to us with great gentleness, helping us to relax and discuss our problems. It was both reassuring and surprising to discover that our problems were not so exceptional. We felt so encouraged from the very first meeting. Emma worked patiently and persistently with us. Now, with a beautiful little boy, we have a great deal to thank her for! We are very glad to hear Emma has written this book. It will be a great benefit to couples.

Acknowledgements

To our very special children, Kate and Jack. Thank you for your constant encouragement not to give up. You are so full of hope and I am so proud of you. One day, when you are old enough, I hope you will read this book and be proud of me too.

Thank you to all my family who have championed me along this journey. With special thanks to my Dad, who painstakingly edited the first draft for me. Thank you for your time and your continued support about the need for such a book.

Special thanks to Ali Hull, my editor. I really could not have completed this book without you. You are a true genius. Your wisdom and expertise has been invaluable, and your refreshing attitude to the subject matter from day one has kept me enthused and determined to follow this through to the end.

To Suzi Hull and the team at Hullo Creative: thank you for embracing this book with warmth, enthusiasm and creative excellence. Your input has transformed the text into something truly beautiful.

To Nicky and Sila Lee, thank you for your warmth and encouragement. The work that you do is so valuable and I feel very privileged that you have taken the time to walk through this journey with me.

To Kevan Wylie; an internationally renowned leader in the field of sexual medicine. I feel very privileged and grateful that you have supported this book in the way that you have. Thank you.

To Dr Isobel White, thank you for your friendship and support, and for your generous giving of your time to read and give feedback on the manuscript.

To Nikki Lewis, Rob Walker and the team at London Bridge Urology. Thank you for creating an environment that feels like my second home. I feel very fortunate to be part of your team and really value all the support that you give me.

To Mr Rick Popert and Dr Cath Rodgers, thank you for your clinical expertise in the relevant chapters. To work with you and have access to your wealth of experience is an incredible resource.

ACKNOWLEDGEMENTS

To the late Dr Graham Jackson, this book would not have been possible if I had not had the opportunity to work with you, and set up the Male Cardiovascular Health Clinic. I will always be grateful for this and the generous way in which you shared your incredible knowledge. Thank you.

Archie and Sam Coates, thank you for your friendship, leadership and vision, and for believing in me and trusting me with this sensitive subject.

Steve and Mandy Marshall-Taylor, thank you for your friendship, and for welcoming me so warmly to play a part in the wonderful family life courses that you run.

To Mark and Liz Warom, thank you for your love, encouragement and laughter. Your friendship is very special to me.

To Celia Cullum. Thank you, Ceals, for always being there for me. You are one in a million.

Special thanks to my dear friends Zannah Crow, Suzi Lambert, and Penelope Schmidt-Uili. Your wisdom, prayers and fun have kept me going through all the highs and lows of writing this book and your encouragement has kept me in there to the end.

To my special friends Philippa Goddard and Alice Gurney. Your prayers, support and friendship have meant so much to me over the years. Thank you for all that you have given me.

To Becky Habba, thank you for your listening ear, and for your endless enthusiasm every step of this journey.

Thank you to all those that have written endorsements for this book. I approached you for your wisdom and expertise and to have that is such a blessing.

Thank you to Harry Ingrams, Patrick Knowles, Giles Lambert and Hannah Turpin for your creative input and invaluable advice along the way.

Thank you to all my other dear friends; there are too many to name personally. Thank you for your interest and enthusiasm and for regularly reminding me that such a book is very much needed. Your encouragement has picked me up when I have wavered and for that I am so grateful.

FOREWORD

I have known Emma as a colleague and a friend for over two decades. When she approached me to discuss this book, I was unaware of the strong Christian faith that is central to her life. I soon appreciated that her expertise in the field of sexual medicine makes her the ideal author for it. Talking about sex does not happen easily for many people, even in today's modern society, yet it is central to maintaining intimacy and happiness for many couples.

This book helps to share the message that if we can acknowledge the importance of good and comfortable sex early within our relationships, then if things go wrong for whatever reason, the topic can be discussed without too much fear or embarrassment. Emma provides concise and accurate information that will allow the reader to understand the importance of attending to sexual and relationship issues early, before their impact becomes significant, and that this can be done compassionately and without blame or ridicule.

This book offers insight and assistance on resolving many common issues, and fills a gap in the marketplace, providing an excellent resource for Christians who recognise and respect the needs of their partners. It provides further information into numerous topics that are sometimes difficult to share with our partners, friends or pastors. Emma has written this book to allow the reader to explore aspects of their needs and diversity safely, and I hope that you find it both helpful and enjoyable.

Kevan Wylie

MD FRCP FRCPsych FRCOG FRSPH FECSM

Retired Professor of Sexual Medicine, Sheffield.

President, European Federation of Sexology (2017-2020).

Immediate Past President, World Association for Sexual Health (2017-2021)

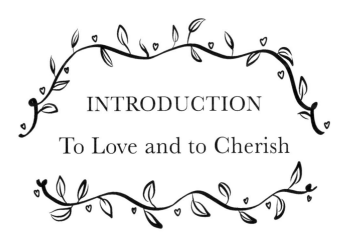

INTRODUCTION
To Love and to Cherish

*Trust in the LORD with all your heart and lean not on your
own understanding; in all your ways submit to him and
he will make your paths straight.*

Proverbs 3:5–6

After many years working in the National Health Service (NHS), I now run a private clinic in a London Hospital seeing men and women, singly and in couples, who present with a range of sexual and relationship problems.

I am a Christian, and for a long time I have been aware that many of the problems I see within my hospital clinic are the very same problems faced by many Christian couples. Over the last few years, I have worked with such couples in my church and further afield. I do not offer long-term therapy because it would mix my professional and social boundaries but we meet informally, as I would with a friend, and I try to help them understand their difficulties and how they might seek the appropriate treatment. This book is specifically aimed at Christians, because faith offers a strength we can draw on that is greater than our own. I want to offer practical advice and to acknowledge we believe in a God who provides hope, comfort and encouragement, particularly in difficult times.

Having said that, you do not have to be a Christian to read this book. Even if you do not have a faith or you have a different faith, you may find the Christian references give you comfort and encouragement, or you may decide to skip over these and focus on the aspects of the book that feel most relevant to you. Likewise, although I am a Christian, this in no way hinders the service I provide to patients that I see in my professional capacity within my hospital clinic.

The focus of this book is directed at married heterosexual couples and I have incorporated wedding vows taken from the Church of England marriage service, and considered what these might mean in practice. Having said that, the wider Christian community is not simply made up of married heterosexual couples. It encompasses huge diversity. However you categorise yourself, God has created us to be *sensual* beings and to celebrate the unique wonder of our bodies, whether we are sexually active or not. I want to value and celebrate that, and hope everyone who reads this book can take something valuable away with them, whatever life stage they are at.

For reasons of space, there are many challenges individuals and couples face that I have not covered; issues that we often do not talk about openly in the Christian community but which are important. These might be to do with sexual orientation or gender identity. It can be painful and lonely, for an individual or a couple, if the issues they are wrestling with are ignored or side-lined.

If this is you, then remember that you are not alone. God cannot be shocked and He never shames us. You can talk to Him about your sadness, your fears, and where to seek help. God wants, above everything else, to be in a relationship with us. Sometimes when we face challenges as Christians we can withdraw from our church communities, especially if we find it difficult to show our vulnerability. If this is you then I would encourage you to try to find a church community where you can be authentic and feel loved by those around you, whatever you are facing. God has designed us to live in community and support each other as we face these challenges together. Chapter 5 considers how and where to seek professional help and I have listed some organisations in Appendix 5 that may offer support and further information.

The seasons of sex and intimacy

'For this reason a man shall leave his father and mother and shall be joined inseparably to his wife, and the two shall become one flesh.'

Matthew 19:5

The Bible describes marriage as a wonderful creation by God, and one of the gifts He has given to help this closeness is sexual intimacy. However, sex is not always easy, and it has different seasons. Maybe it was once passionate and exciting (spring), but it has gone through being fulfilling (summer) to boring (autumn). Or something has changed radically and now it is winter. If we understand these seasons are normal, in all marriages, then we can be better prepared for them, and work together as an "intimate team" when the snow comes. I will explain the concept of the intimate team in Chapter 1.

The National Survey of Sexual Attitudes and Lifestyles 3 (Natsal-3)[1] is one of largest and most detailed global studies of sexual behaviour. Three of these studies have been done in the UK, and all of these studies have provided us with valuable information about individual experiences, views, and behaviours. The most recent was carried out between September 2010 and August 2012, and it interviewed 15,162 men and women, aged between 16 and 74.

The studies remind us that we all face many of the same challenges and difficulties relating to sex. How do we keep passion alive? How do we desire what we already "have"? The research showed that one in four men and one in four women, who were in a relationship, said they do not share the same level of interest in sex as their partner.

Almost one in six people said they had a health condition that had affected their sex life in the past year but few had sought any type of professional help. So how do we learn to roll with the physical and emotional punches of life, such as breast cancer, prostate cancer, infertility, and mental health issues? And then there are more specific difficulties, such as unconsummated marriage, erection problems, ejaculatory problems, painful sex (dyspareunia), low desire, addiction to pornography, and infidelity. The study showed that one in five men and women in a relationship said that their partner had experienced sexual difficulties in the past year.

This book is designed to equip you to face all of these challenges.

I have divided the book into two parts. I would advise all readers to read Part I, which incorporates chapters 1–5. These cover important information for everyone, whether experiencing a sexual problem or not. Part II then moves on to specific problems.

So we start with Chapter 1, looking at communicating in marriage, not just on sexual matters, and the importance of becoming an intimate team. Chapter 2 considers the importance of understanding our bodies so that we can learn to give and receive pleasure, and describes how usual sexual arousal works. Chapter 3 looks at important ways to increase sexual enjoyment as a couple and to nurture lifelong desire in marriage. Chapter 4 covers the damaging impact of pornography on a relationship. You may not feel that pornography is an issue for you, but it is impacting the way our children are learning about sex and it is sadly becoming an acceptable part of our culture. It is also a huge problem for Christians and will almost certainly be impacting someone you know, so awareness of it is important for all of us. Chapter 5 covers why and how to seek help, what you can expect from a GP or clinic, and how to find a sex therapist.

What if I have a sexual problem?

Chapters 6–11 cover specific sexual difficulties and anything your GP or sex therapist might do for that specific issue.

When I meet with a couple with a sexual problem, my role is a bit like that of a nurse working in an Accident and Emergency (A&E) department. In A&E, a triage nurse will usually quickly diagnose your immediate need. Could you be seen by your GP? Do you need immediate but non-urgent care, or urgent life-saving treatment? I perform a similar role with the couples I meet, and ask myself the following questions:

- Do I sense the marriage is strong and, with help, this couple could fix the problem themselves?

- Do they need treatment to help manage a physical or emotional issue that is preventing or impacting sex?

- Have they had a good sexual relationship historically, but a life event has had an effect?

- Is this couple in crisis, needing immediate counselling?

We live in a sexualised society and feel real pressure that sex should always be spontaneous, satisfying, and exciting. Our bodies should work just as we expect them to. Couples who find this is not the case for them can struggle to get help and often feel ashamed. Many have lived with the problems for years, never discussing them with even close family or friends. Often they only make a concerted effort to seek treatment when they are desperate.

My professional title is Psychosexual Nurse Specialist, which combines the role of nurse and therapist. This combined skill set has been useful because I am able to consider possible underlying physical factors that might be impacting someone's ability to engage in and enjoy sex, and to think about the psychological and relational aspects. I want to give you enough information so you can "triage" yourself: determine what the problem is, what type of help you need and how to access it. That may involve practical steps that you can do on your own or as a couple; or you may need to get help from either a medical specialist and/or a sex and relationship therapist. I have suggested various books and resources that my patients, whether they have a faith or not, find really helpful. It is important to note that these resources are not necessarily written or produced by those with a Christian faith, and for some, this may challenge their 'moral' compass. I cannot discuss this with readers as I can with those I meet, so do use your own discernment, take advantage of what is helpful and avoid whatever does not sit comfortably with you.

Many couples say they wish they had had information about how to manage sexual difficulties at the start of their relationship, so they could have dealt with the issues more quickly. Identifying a problem promptly and putting an action plan in place can stop it from escalating. When we are struggling, we want clear directions and I plan to provide these. People don't want lots of detail to wade through, so explanations will be brief, exercises will be simple, and there will be plenty of suggested helpful resources.

There are many reasons why people have sex. It can be to show love, to create new life, to self-soothe or to release tension. Or it might be to fuel an addiction, to earn money or in response to fear or coercion. The same act can create very different experiences and meanings, depending on the reasons for engaging in it. It is important to acknowledge this. The Natsal-3 study reported that one in ten women and one in 71 men, aged thirteen or above, had experienced non-volitional sex: sex against their will. The mean age at which this occurred was sixteen for men, and eighteen for women.

As you read this book, you may become aware that you are struggling with painful and complex problems, which are unlikely to be resolved with the self-help/couple strategies outlined in the following chapters. You may have experienced sexual abuse or trauma. If so, do not lose heart but seek professional help. I have outlined some tips on looking for a therapist in Chapter 5. You may wish to revisit some of the self-help strategies in this book when you have dealt with wider issues that would otherwise continue to hold you back, either individually or as a couple.

As Christians, we know that God has promised never to leave us alone. As a loving Father, He draws us close to Him, whatever we are facing. He is an all-weather God, an ever-present source of hope and comfort. I hope you can use this book to enrich your relationship, with a realism about the potential for the changing seasons and the wonderful opportunity for greater intimacy that this can create with your spouse.

May the God of hope fill you with all joy and peace as you trust in him, so that you may overflow with hope by the power of the Holy Spirit.

Romans 15:13

References

1. www.natsal.ac.uk/home.aspx

PART ONE

Understanding Our Bodies
and Nurturing Sexual Intimacy

CHAPTER ONE

For Better, for Worse: Effective Communication

Praise be to the God and Father of our Lord Jesus Christ, the Father of compassion and the God of all comfort, who comforts us in all our troubles, so that we can comfort those in any trouble with the comfort we ourselves receive from God.

2 Corinthians 1:3-4

The most important attribute of a good sexual relationship is effective communication. Effective communication is important in all our relationships because it ensures we are able to make ourselves heard and understood. As humans, we strive to be known: *really* heard, seen, and understood, particularly by those that are closest to us – our partners. But this is often hard, especially if we have difficult things to say. If we learn to do it well, however, we will have the tools to tackle anything in our marriage, including sexual difficulties, and be honest, vulnerable, and truly *ourselves*. Most of us strive to be known by our partners just as we are, so we can experience deep emotional intimacy and connection. We want to be loved for being us, warts and all.

The subject of communication is a huge one and in this book I can only introduce some important principles for nurturing effective communication. Hopefully, these will get you thinking and talking to your partner about how you communicate as a couple.

Good communication means articulating what we feel, what we want, and what we need. It sounds simple but it's challenging. A whole set of feelings and experiences will have shaped us into who we are. Some will be positive, others difficult and painful. We carry within us messages we have formulated about ourselves and those we have absorbed from our parents or caregivers as we have grown up. Some of these are affirming: "We were so thrilled when you were born." "We are so proud of you." "You are really lovely." Others hurt: "You are such a disappointment to us." "You never get it right." We carry many of these messages unconsciously, which can make their effect harder to understand. These silent messages have been wired into our core and they can impact the way we experience the world. We need to be aware that we all carry these early messages and their effects. The patterns of behaviour they will lead to can be helpful or hurtful in all our relationships but particularly with our partners.

To help the reader understand the issues of communication, I am going to introduce the ideas of a particular model of psychotherapy. Don't be put off: I will keep it simple. I will discuss practical tools later in the chapter, but if we can consider some of the deeper underlying emotional challenges, we are more likely to implement lasting change. These concepts will help as you address the issues in your marriage, whether they relate to sex or not.

Transactional Analysis (TA) is a school of psychotherapy that I have found really helpful in my work with couples who want to improve how they communicate with one another. TA is a very accessible model, easy both to understand and put into practice. Its central model is the "ego state model", right at the heart of how we think about communication. An ego state is a combination of the way we think, feel, and potentially behave and these consistently occur together. Eric Berne defines three ego states: **Parent**, **Adult**, and **Child**.[1] The ego states do not correspond to being a parent, an adult or a child; they are descriptions of how we might be experiencing and processing the world at a given time.

The Parent ego state is concerned with ways of thinking, feeling, and behaving, taken from what we have absorbed unconsciously and observed consciously from the authority figures in our past. The Parent ego state is often seen as the rule maker, the teacher, and the nurturer: "Do not run into the road; a car might hit you." In this sense, it can be supportive and caring, but it can also be critical and limiting: "Careful, you never get it right!" This state is affected not only by what we observed happening but also by what we did not see. So, for example, if we never saw our parents cry, we might have learnt, on some level, that it is not okay to show emotion. This might have been reinforced if we struggled not to cry as a child and were praised for not giving way to tears. The Parent ego state can be seen as a set of permissions ("This is okay to do"), injunctions ("Don't do this") or denials ("This is not acceptable").

The Adult ego state directly focuses on what is going on now, without interference from the Parent or the Child, and involves the thoughts, feelings, and behaviours associated with dealing with the present. I think of it as the logical, reasonable, and fair voice. An example might be being moved to tears by something emotional and allowing yourself to cry freely, recognising that this is a perfectly acceptable response to sadness.

The Child ego state is thoughts, feelings, and behaviours associated with our past. Of particular relevance here are our early years. Again, these thoughts, feelings, and behaviours will have developed in relation to our main caregivers (usually our parents) and other significant "grown up" figures. We might have learnt that the world is an exciting place full of opportunity, waiting to be discovered. Or we might have learnt that we have to be seen and not heard. We might have learnt that we need to be a very good little boy or girl because if we can keep others around us "okay" then we will be "okay." In families like these, the overarching thoughts, feelings, and behaviours for the child are often about reading another's behaviours and adapting to those around them.

This can be even more prevalent if we have grown up with unpredictable parents. For example, if one or both parents were alcoholics, abusive or struggled with mental health issues, then we might have learnt, "If I sit here quietly and do not move, nobody will shout at me or hit me." This is the child's way of trying to gain some control in an environment that feels out of control. This can be a very helpful "survival" mode for that child when they are young. However, if they take this adapted behaviour into adulthood, they are less likely to get their own needs met. This can lead to resentment and sometimes a person can then behave like a victim: "It is okay for everyone else, I never get what I want." The additional challenge may be that the adult actually does not know what they want, because they have never focused on their needs. Before we articulate our needs, we need to be able to get in touch with what these are. Personal therapy is a great environment to focus on what our needs might be and then look at how we get these met.

When we think about ego states we can either *be* in an ego state, acting as our parent figure did ("Pull my shoulders back, stiff upper lip, do not cry") or acting as we did as a child ("I don't want to go to the restaurant my friend has suggested but I will go along with it. I don't know how to say no and I don't know where I want to go anyway.")

We can also be *influenced* by an inner voice in our head, related to an ego state. For example, I might experience the world and behave like my mother (Parent) or I may hear her voice in my head saying "Do not do X." In another situation, rather than being *like* my mother, I might start experiencing the world and behaving as I used to when I was *around* her (Child). I will give you an example to illustrate this.

Let's imagine that I have gone on a hike with a friend. It's a hot day and I would like to stop for a drink. I might say something like "I'm feeling really hot and tired. There is a nice pub coming up, so shall we stop for a drink?" I am saying what I need, at that moment, from my Adult ego state, and asking that those needs should be met. I am able to articulate what is going on for me in that moment.

But if I had grown up with a parent who suggested I "always make a fuss", then I might feel unable to say that I was thirsty and would like a drink. The voice in my head would be saying again, "Don't make a fuss." Instead of acting from my Adult ego state and asking for a drink, I would be feeling the way I did as a child. Also, my Child ego state has a *stronger* voice than my Adult ego state. The sense that I must not make a fuss is stronger than my rational voice that says it is perfectly fine to ask for a drink, to ask for what I need.

Alternatively, instead of being in my Child ego state, I might square my shoulders, as my parents used to, and just push on through until I get to the end of the hike, even though I wanted to stop for a drink.

If I take this "Do not make a fuss" attitude into my marriage, then I will probably still be unable to say what I need but will feel taken for granted when my partner does not automatically understand what I need, without me having to ask them. This is just one simple example, but it illustrates how complex a relationship can be, when two people come together, each with their own set of pre-recorded feelings, experiences, and beliefs. We all fluctuate regularly between all the ego states, and this is completely normal, but it does mean that communication becomes very muddy, clouding what we hear from our partners and how we feel. TA therapy often focuses on strengthening the Adult voice, and in order to do this, we need to understand some of the familiar Parent and Child voices that get in the way. Really effective and honest communication happens when *both* partners can talk from an Adult place. Then we are more likely to give equal value to our differing views and, even if we do not end up agreeing, we will both feel listened to, able to articulate our needs, and above all respected.

SEASONS OF SEX & INTIMACY

I am going to give you another example to demonstrate the ego state model. I have purposely made this about sex, as this can often feel like a particularly difficult topic to talk about.

Setting the scene

Ben and Sarah have not had sexual intimacy for two months. Ben has a new job and he's quite preoccupied and stressed. Sarah feels rejected. The last couple of times she tried to initiate sex, Ben said he was too tired and wanted to go to sleep. They are planning a weekend away and Sarah is hoping that the time without the children will include sex. So, as she is packing, she says, "I'm really looking forward to the weekend. It will be nice to have some time together and hopefully you will not feel so stressed." Sarah grew up in a loving family but it was not acceptable to ask for things. You got what you were given. Feeling rejected by Ben has hurt her, but she has not found a way of talking about it and is worried she will upset him.

Ben is sensitive about the whole subject of sex because he feels that he has let Sarah down. He grew up in a family with high expectations, where failure was not an option, so he is very harsh on himself. His internal voice is one of a critical parent (perhaps his father) and he regularly berates himself for his shortcomings. When he hears Sarah's comments, he gets defensive, thinking that she is criticising him; the words "Can't even keep your wife happy!" run through his mind. Feeling hurt, he retorts, "It's fine for you; you have no idea what pressure I'm under. You only have to look after the kids!" And of course, she now feels hurt as well.

The interaction

At this stage, the couple could go one of two ways. The first one does not go well. Sarah feels desperately hurt by Ben. She feels he has told her off in a way she was told off as a child. She particularly remembers a time when she was five years old and commented to her father that the ice cream in the shop looked nice. Her father responded, "You're not having one!" As Ben makes his remark, she suddenly feels so exasperated that she throws all the clothes she was packing onto the floor and says, "I don't even want to go away now. It's not like we will have sex!" Then she storms out of the room.

Now both Sarah and Ben feel angry and hurt. Neither is in Adult and the weekend away hangs in the balance. It is so easy to identify with this situation, although naturally the details of each couple's issues will vary. In the heat of the moment, both Sarah and Ben retreat into their separate spaces to ponder how mean their spouse is and how misunderstood they are. The sad thing here is that both positions are valid and real for that person. But to understand how the other is feeling, we need to put our own hurt and pride to one side and listen to our partner. This is not easy, especially if their comments have brought up early painful feelings of shame, judgement, or injustice.

Another difficulty is that we may need to accept that our partner is feeling something that we cannot identify with. For example, Ben will not necessarily be able to relate to how Sarah remembers her father speaking to her about the ice cream, but for her it was and continues to feel incredibly painful. She felt verbally slapped down by her father then, and she feels slapped down by her husband now. Nor will she necessarily be able to understand that her encouraging comment symbolised something else for Ben. It took him to a young place too, where he never felt good enough and it was always implied he could do better.

Both of their experiences of witnessing how their parents resolved conflicts may influence where they go from here. Perhaps they go away for the weekend, but the atmosphere is cool and distant. They do not have sex and both come home feeling lost in their marriage. Perhaps they do not even make it as far as the weekend, as one or the other of them refuses to go after the row.

The resolution

However, if both parties can recognise they are not in Adult and the hurt they are feeling has tapped into something much deeper, then perhaps they will be able to share this understanding of themselves and what happened between them. This is not easy and it takes courage: and we do not always want to do so when we feel wronged and vulnerable. But if the couple are able to come from an Adult place, then the conversation might go like this…

An hour or so has passed since Sarah stormed out. She goes and finds Ben.

"I'm feeling hurt about what has happened tonight. We have been so looking forward to this weekend away and I feel that it would be good if we can try and talk about it, either this evening or tomorrow. Otherwise I think the whole weekend could be ruined."

The pull for Ben is to stay in Child and retort, "What's the point? You said you didn't want to go anyway."

This will make Sarah feel angry and hurt all over again, as she has set aside her pride to approach Ben, despite feeling wronged herself. But if she can stay in Adult…

"I do want to go. I said that because I felt hurt."

The honesty of Sarah's comments connects with Ben and he moves into Adult. "I felt hurt too. It would be sad if we didn't go. I agree we need to talk about it, but I have a really early start tomorrow, and I cannot think straight tonight. How do you feel about us leaving it until tomorrow?"

Sarah would have liked to have discussed it immediately, but she appreciates the change in Ben's tone and sees how drained he looks. "Okay. I'll make sure the kids are in bed on time tomorrow evening and then we can talk undisturbed."

Ben in turn appreciates that Sarah has listened to what he needs. His heart is softened and the anger he felt has gone. He does not feel got at, as he had done earlier in the evening. He smiles at Sarah and says, "I really do want to go away; I've been looking forward to it."

Sarah responds, "Me too."

Reflections

If this were a film, they would go to bed, fall into each other's arms, and make love. But life is not a film. The reality is they both feel bruised by what has been said, but they have a plan. When they sit down the next night to talk, they have had a day to think about what each of them was feeling in that moment. The challenge here is for both Ben and Sarah to stay in Adult. To do this they need to try to articulate what each of them has been feeling, in a way that feels unthreatening and open. By open, I mean ready to hear the other's perspective and to give this view equal value and respect, even if their views are different. This can be a real challenge but, in my experience, the more we practise this, the easier it is, and it then becomes a familiar way to communicate.

During the conversation, they untangle how one seemingly innocent comment led to such an outburst from Ben. He shares how he has been feeling about the stresses of his work, which he has felt Sarah has not understood. Sarah explains that she has not been given the chance to understand because Ben has not shared them with her; a point with which he agrees. For the first time, she is able to share her sadness about the lack of sexual intimacy and how she has started to wonder if Ben still finds her attractive, post-children. A lot of ground is covered, some of it difficult, but the couple emerge a bit shaken perhaps, yet also comforted in their ability to speak their own truth and be *properly* heard.

Having read this, you may be able to begin to identify with some of the feelings relating to the Child and Parent ego states: being like one of your parents, replaying strong critical voices that put you down, or having to over-adapt to keep everyone around you happy, which means you never get your own needs met. The more you commit to reflecting on what you are feeling at a given time and try to pinpoint what is resonating for you, the more adept you will become at realising what lies behind your strong reactions. You will need to find time to talk about this, because over time it will help to identify stumbling blocks for you both, as well as flashpoints.

During my TA training, I became aware how angry I can feel about certain seemingly innocuous things, which other people did not even seem to notice. Over time I realised that what was being pulled in me was a sense of outrage when something was not fair. I am one of six children, and although my parents did their utmost to be fair, there were times when I felt an injustice had been done. I am aware that the strength of my feelings as an indignant three-year-old can regularly replay in my life now. This revelation has helped me understand why I am so affected by seemingly trivial things. In understanding this, I am able to say to myself: "Ah – Emma when she was three!" The feeling does not always go away, but it loses much of its power because I understand it.

Practising self-awareness, understanding yourself and how you fit together with your partner – this is an essential ongoing project that can revolutionise your marriage.

Communication: some practical tips

Weekly meetings

Rather than allowing issues to fester, couples can regularly set aside time to talk every week. My husband and I call this our weekly meeting. Most businesses have them: why not marriages? It does not have to be arduous (it might even include a glass of wine), but if we are regularly connected with our partner – aware of what is going on in each other's lives – then we can work out some of the smaller issues as they come up.

At one of our weekly meetings, my husband mentioned that it bothered him that he regularly had to go to the supermarket at the weekends to get groceries. He thought that we had agreed that I would try where possible to do this in the week so that we had more time for fun things at the weekends with our children.

My first instinct was to feel criticised: momentarily I felt like being defensive about all the other things I have been doing (I was not in Adult). I took a second to process this and realised that actually he was right. We had agreed this, and it was perfectly fair for him to query why it was not happening. In Adult I could recognise the validity of his point. Equally in Adult, I could also have said (if I had felt I needed to), "That's not practical now because of X, Y, Z, so can we renegotiate this?" We have reinstated the plan and our weekends are much freer.

You are not listening

It is also worth checking ourselves out with our partner as a conversation proceeds. How do they perceive our tone of voice, body language, and facial expressions? When I am listening to someone, I usually look quite intense and focus on the person's eyes as they speak. My husband is very different. He will often look into the distance or at the floor but rarely at my face. Sometimes I have said to him that he looks bored while I am talking. He has quite genuinely said that he is just processing what I have been saying, and to his credit he is able to repeat back what I have said almost word for word. He just listens in a different way.

Equally, there have been occasions when I have been told that my body language has looked quite defensive and that has surprised me. I had not been feeling defensive, but I had crossed my arms because I was cold. It is worth checking these things out as they happen, because of course there may be a time that crossing my arms *does* actually reveal a defensiveness that I am unaware of, until it is brought to my attention.

What secret plan?

We all have "secret plans": things we might like to do, but they remain unsaid. For example, I might think how nice it would be to have a lie-in at the weekend and then go for a family walk followed by lunch. I plan the day in my head, I think about which pub we might go to, but I do not share any of this with my husband. When the weekend comes, I mention the "plan" as if my husband knows all about it, and I am frustrated when he does not get on board! In turn, he has a secret plan of his own: a bike ride, taking the children swimming, and watching the football. So many arguments could be avoided if couples shared their secret plans, not just for the weekend but for life generally. Negotiation would mean both parties end up doing some of what they want to do, and this could stop anger and resentment.

White flag

It is important to remember that what we say to someone can build them up or tear them down. I have met a number of patients over the years who have struggled with sexual problems, performance anxiety, and self-esteem issues. When I take a history from them we can often trace these back to something that a partner or spouse has said, whether to be cruel or make a joke, and other times completely unwittingly. The comments might be about the size of a man's penis. Meant in jest, it actually feeds into an existing insecurity. It might be a careless comment about a partner gaining weight. It might be a comment about a past relationship that sows a seed of doubt about the marriage or the sex life of the couple.

If a couple works together as a team, then they should be able to address sensitive issues in the marriage, such as weight gain. However, this can only be explored if the relationship has a strong foundation and each spouse knows they are loved, respected, and listened to by their partner. Such issues have to be very gently approached, sometimes with the help of a therapist. It is so sad when I work with an individual who has been deeply scarred by an insensitive or cruel comment. As Christians, we need to choose our words wisely, and if we feel that we want to retaliate and lash out with something hurtful, then we need to walk away or exercise self-discipline. We cannot take our words back and so we must only give them out mindfully and with great care.

You are more likely to have a constructive discussion if you are not angry. Anger is a very important emotion, signalling something is wrong, but communicating effectively when you are angry is almost impossible, and this is often when we can lash out with unkind comments. We can experience anger in all of our ego states – Parent, Adult and Child – but we are more likely to act out impulsively from Parent or Child. If communication in your relationship regularly ends in angry outbursts, find a time with your spouse when you are both calm so that you can locate where the anger is coming from. Some couples will use a "white flag" system. This means that when their arguments stop being constructive, one or both parties hold up a white flag and both walk away. The discussion will be resumed later when they both feel more in control.

What did you say?

Properly listening to our partners can be very difficult. We need to put aside our own thoughts and judgements and place our partner centre-stage. Often the temptation is to interrupt, make "helpful" suggestions, and impose our wonderful solutions onto their problems. Concentrated listening can be sacrificial. Sometimes the desire to soothe them is born out of the discomfort we experience when we are exposed to another's pain. If I soothe them, then I do not need to sit with this raw, unmanageable pain myself.

I once chatted with a friend who was unable to have children. She talked about her numerous attempts at infertility treatment and how painful each failed cycle was. I found her visible distress almost unbearable. I so wanted to comfort her because it would ultimately make it easier for me. I had on the tip of my tongue, "Have you considered adoption?" when she said to me: "The worst thing is, everyone keeps asking me if I have considered adoption – they just cannot bear to sit with my grief."

I know just how that feels…

There can also be a temptation to say things such as "I know just how that feels because that happened to me." We manage to creep onstage. Suddenly the spotlight is shared, and we are giving advice about how to make things better. The truth is we are never going to fully understand what a given situation feels like for another person; however, we can be available to them, to listen to what it is like for them. A very simple and effective technique, especially if we have a tendency to want to jump in and "rescue", is to ask our partner at the start of a conversation, "What do you need from me?" This will depend on what the conversation is about, but this way you can ensure you are available to your partner in the way they need you. They will often say, "I just need you to listen."

Set aside time

If you anticipate that a conversation is going to be hard, for example talking about something very personal such as sex, then prepare for it. When you are both calm, explain there is something you want to discuss, and you recognise it is not an easy subject. Give your partner the heads-up so they do not feel unprepared.

If we consider the couple from earlier, Ben and Sarah, Sarah might ask, "Is this a good time to talk?" If Ben says it is, she might go on, "It isn't easy to talk about sex and we rarely do, but I'm sad because we are not having it much, and it feels to me that something has changed." The conversation may then comfortably lead into addressing the issue, but if Ben responds with something like "This feels very heavy, and I'm not in the mood to discuss it" then Sarah will need to negotiate a time when they will be able to talk about this.

It is important that the partner raising the issue does not feel brushed off or unheard. When we say "I feel sad" we are owning our emotions. We are not blaming the other person for the way we are feeling. So Sarah is not saying to Ben, "You make me sad because you don't fancy me." We should recognise no one can *make* us feel any emotion: sadness, anger, happiness or fear. It is true that people can invite us to feel a particular emotion, and sometimes those invitations can be pretty strong! However, we are in control of how we react to others, including what we think and how we feel about them. Sarah might say, "When I approach you in bed for a cuddle and you brush me off, I feel really sad." She is owning her feelings. It is much less threatening for Ben to hear, because he is not being blamed for the way she feels. She is not saying, "You make me feel really unattractive when you turn away."

Ben may still feel defensive and respond from Parent or Child with something like "You are always going on about sex. Give it a rest." Then Sarah might be tempted to respond with something equally hurtful, such as "Don't blame me if I stray then!" It might be hard for her to stay in Adult, but she needs to do so, if she wants to move to a place of resolution. She might say, "It took a lot of courage tonight to bring the sex thing up. I understand if you don't want to talk about it now, but I want to talk about it at some point, because I don't want to go on feeling this sad. Our marriage is precious to me and I want to work out how to make it better for us both." The hope is that this will connect with Ben, and conversation, however challenging, can happen.

It may be that as you read this, you recognise that it is hard for you to be in Adult, and you do not know how to access this part of you. If so, and the Transactional Analysis model appeals to you, then explore these themes more in individual therapy. A large part of TA therapy is often about helping the client strengthen their Adult ego state, which can be really helpful in many aspects of our lives. Or if you are interested in simply finding out more about TA, there is a great two-day introductory course called the 101, which is run nationally. It is open to anyone interested. Do the course as a couple so you can understand the theory together. It will enrich your marriage and all the other relationships in your life. There is more information in Appendix 5 on courses and TA therapists.

Love languages

A book I regularly recommend to couples who might be struggling with relational disharmony is *The Five Love Languages* by Gary Chapman.[2] You may already be familiar with this Christian author who has written a series of books for couples and families. He focuses on how we give love to, and receive love from, our partners, through five "love languages." These languages are: physical affection, gifts, acts of service, quality time, and words of affirmation. Often we demonstrate our love to our spouse in the way *we* like to receive it, but this is not necessarily how *they* would like to receive it. This can lead to hurt on both sides. We may need to be intentional in order to discover our spouse's love language, especially if it is not ours. This is an excellent book and I encourage you to read it.

What is an "intimate team"?

Sex and relationship therapists Michael Metz and Barry McCarthy are the authors of the book *Enduring Desire* and have coined the term "intimate team".[3] They see the intimate team as the foundation of building lifelong desire in a relationship, and it means creating "a healthy, cooperative relationship." Their book is a guide to nurturing lifelong intimacy, and this also includes another concept that can help us do this: the "good enough sex model" which I will touch upon in Chapter 3. Creating an intimate team is, they say, the most important thing a couple can do to nurture intimacy and manage any sexual problems. But what does it mean?

Creating an intimate team is partly about placing a high priority on the marital relationship, above children, work, extended family, leisure activities, and indeed church. Your spouse needs to know they are your most important priority. This might be difficult for some couples. Some people find it hard to separate from their parents; others find, when children come along, they take priority.

The four key components to creating an intimate team, according to Metz and McCarthy, are: emotional intimacy, communication intimacy, commitment intimacy, and sexual intimacy. Couples need to be able to share on a deep level with each other, and to communicate truthfully, lovingly, and trustingly. If the couple have an effective communication intimacy in place, where they can communicate their own needs, listen to the needs of their partners, and acknowledge those needs, then if there are sexual problems, the communication skills are already in place to discuss those problems and possible solutions.

For example, let us consider this scenario. Jane is being treated for breast cancer and the chemotherapy has sent her into an early menopause. The sudden hormonal changes have significantly impacted her desire to be sexual with her husband Tim. When they have tried to make love, it has been very painful for her. If the couple are functioning as an intimate team, then Jane will be able to listen to Tim telling her how much he is missing their usual sexual contact. They will be able to discuss solutions: perhaps she will touch him purely to give him sexual pleasure. Both will understand that she does not have to respond sexually at this point if she does not feel able. Or maybe she is missing physical contact with him but fears if she instigates this, there will be pressure to be sexual and she has no desire for this at the moment. If Tim knows this, the couple can agree how to get Jane's need for touch met as well. The couple will recognise this is likely to be a temporary phase, as Jane moves through her treatment, but in the present, they can negotiate what they both need now. This is particularly important with something like a cancer diagnosis, where both partners will have a whole host of emotions, such as fear, sadness, and anger, and drawing together to share these is particularly important at such a vulnerable time.

If you do not feel your relationship is working at this level, then maybe *Enduring Desire* might help you, or maybe couple counselling or individual therapy might be appropriate. You will find more information about where to seek help in Chapter 5.

How do we talk about sex?

So how do I talk about sex with my partner? If we invest time in honing our communication skills in the other aspects of our relationship, then talking about sex should be no different, and there should be no special requirements. It will be a natural evolution of a maturing intimacy. The better we get at communicating, the closer we feel, and introducing sex into the discussion will hold no fear or mystery.

I regularly speak at evenings in the church for those who are getting ready for marriage, are already married, or are in a committed relationship. We encourage couples to submit anonymous questions, and many of the same questions come up again and again, suggesting many Christian couples are curious about the same issues:

- How do you keep sexual desire alive in a long-term relationship?
- Is it okay to have anal sex?
- Is it okay to have oral sex?
- Is it okay to role play, or to share fantasies in your marriage?
- What do I say to my partner if I want to try something sexually?
- Should you talk about past sexual experiences in your marriage?
- How do I approach sex if I have had bad sexual experiences in the past?

There is a wide variation in what different Christians believe is acceptable sexual practice (sometimes supported by biblical "proof texts"), but I think that a couple needs to decide for themselves what they feel

30

comfortable with having in their own sexual "toolbox" (see Chapter 3). It will vary from one couple to another. It may include oral sex, or acting out sexual fantasies. Couples need to discuss these issues. My belief is that God is much more interested in *how* the couple functions as a team and come to agree about their sexual repertoire, rather than *what* the repertoire actually includes. God does not blush, and we cannot embarrass Him. Nor does He leave the bedroom when we make love. God cares more about how we honour our partners and uphold our marriage vows, nurturing love and intimacy, than He does about the details of what we do together sexually.

Your sexual choices will also be shaped by how you view God, what you believe is acceptable to Him. As a couple, you can ask God to guide you in this area. God wants us to nurture a partnership that will sustain us for the whole of our married lives. This will include love, respect, honouring our body and each other's. To do this, any sexual act must be:

- consensual: both parties to agree wholeheartedly to participate in the sexual act

- respectful: we listen to the needs and requests of our partner and give them equal value with our own

- pleasurable: loving, an act that deepens our commitment to the relationship

Whatever we do, we must both agree, freely. However much we want to please our partners or resolve our difficulties, sexual intimacy must be free from coercion or fear. This does not mean that sex has to be solemn. Our sexual repertoire will enable us to vary what we might like to do, which often helps to fuel desire and keep passion alive.

Infidelity

Why have I included a section on infidelity in the chapter on communication? Because, in many cases, when one partner has had an affair, the issue is rarely about sex. It is often more about a desire for attention, and as Esther Perel has identified in her research, it is about a need in the "perpetrator" to feel "alive". She also identifies that it is often about what the person who has the affair feels they have lost about themselves, that fuels their desire to stray.[4]

So, if an affair is actually about a need to feel alive, how do we ensure that we stay alive in our marriages? If we are an intimate team, we will need to have this dialogue constantly with our partner. What makes you feel alive? Is it fulfilling a passion, studying, working towards a goal, enjoying the arts, travelling, and many other things?

In order to continue feeling alive, we need to identify those things that fuel us, but also to name those that drain us, corrode us, and stop us becoming the version of ourselves that we desire to be. These conversations also need to happen throughout marriage. Our goals and passions change as we get older and life stages change. An intimate team gives us the communication skills to revisit these questions time and time again. If I am restless in my marriage, then my head is more likely to be turned by another: a colleague at work, a friend, someone at church. At this point, I need to bring this back into the team to discuss it. This will not be easy but is necessary if we are going to remain faithful.

Sometimes friends have raised an eyebrow when I have said my husband and I regularly discuss the subject of infidelity. They seem to think we are somehow less committed or even playing with fire, just by broaching this subject. On the contrary: we are talking about how easily we can get burnt, sometimes so subtly that we have not even realised we are playing with fire in the first place. We are humans and none of us are infallible. We need to be constantly revisiting these discussions in our marriages. What do we need to do for ourselves and what do we need from our partner to feel alive, desired, and anchored to the marriage? As Esther Perel says, many couples only begin to have these conversations when an affair has happened, or is happening. But it is much more constructive to talk about them when the relationship is not in a crisis, but when trust is still strong.

Forsaking all others

Almost without exception, all of us stand before our partner on our wedding day fully believing the vows we make:

"Will you love him, comfort him, honour and protect him, and, forsaking all others, be faithful to him as long as you both shall live?"

"I will!"

"Will you love her, comfort her, honour and protect her, and, forsaking all others, be faithful to her as long as you both shall live?"

"I will!"

If we truly believed it, then what goes wrong? Somewhere along the line we start to lose a sense of who we are in the marriage. Perhaps I feel my husband was once warm, but it does not feel that way now, and I am desperately sad about it and unsure where to turn. Perhaps I disclose this to a friendly male colleague at work. Over coffee, he tells me he is going through similar issues with his wife. We now have a shared intimacy that leaves both parties vulnerable. Or perhaps a man has not had sex with his wife for many months and he is feeling unsure how to broach this subject with her. He feels lost and sad and he shares this with a single woman at church who is feeling vulnerable about being single. Suddenly there is a shared intimacy and both parties are vulnerable.

Generally people do not wake up one morning suddenly feeling lost and sad and then fall into the arms of another. This is a slow process of disengagement and distance being created within the marriage, and to avoid it, we need to keep talking to our partners. This can feel like hard work. But when we look at our wedding vows, they are all about hard work: the good, the bad, the rich, the poor, health, and illness: for better and for worse.

I do believe it is possible for many couples to move forward from an affair and create something good. If you are coming to terms with or recovering from an affair in your marriage, whether it was you who strayed or not, then read Chapter 5 and consider seeing a couples therapist. They will help you to understand what happened between making those marriage vows and now. You can then set in place the keys to creating an intimate team and maybe reconstruct a new partnership that renews trust and nurtures hope.

If you are interested in listening to Esther Perel talk on the subject of affairs, she does an excellent TED talk: www.ted.com/talks/esther_perel_ rethinking_infidelity_a_talk_for_anyone_who_has_ever_loved#t-1275444

Because you are my help, I sing in the shadow of your wings.

Psalm 63:7

References

1. Eric Berne, *Transactional Analysis in Psychotherapy*. (New York: Grove Press, 1961)

2. Gary Chapman, *The Five Love Languages*, (Chicago: Moody Press, 2015)

3. Michael E. Metz and Barry W. McCarthy, *Enduring Desire: Your Guide to Lifelong Intimacy*, (London: Routledge, 2010).

4. Esther Perel, *The State of Affairs: Rethinking Infidelity*, (London: Yellow Kite, 2017).

Recommended reading

Sarah Abell, *Authentic: Relationships From The Inside Out*, (London: Hodder & Stoughton, 2009).

Alain de Botton, *The Course of Love*, (London: Penguin, 2017). This is one of my favourite books. It is a novel about marriage and the author intersperses the text with reflections about what is going on for the couple psychologically.

Nicky and Sila Lee, *The Marriage Book*, (London: Alpha International, 2009).

CHAPTER TWO

Fearfully and Wonderfully Made: How Our Bodies Work

For you created my inmost being; you knit me together in my mother's womb. I praise you because I am fearfully and wonderfully made; your works are wonderful, I know that full well.

Psalm 139:13–14

The next two chapters will concentrate on sex, how we view and enjoy it. This chapter will focus on the importance of understanding our bodies and how they work, usual sexual arousal, and becoming more aware of our own sexual responses. Some people have received very little sex education from their parents or school and learnt a lot more from friends or pornography. Much of this is often misinformation and not helpful, which can result in people having unrealistic expectations about sex and struggling with intimacy, both sexually and emotionally.

Understanding our bodies

From an early age, children will touch their own bodies, including their genitals. It is instinctive and not sexual; children are only ashamed if others make them so. Children can be quite preoccupied with touching their genitals because it feels nice and gives them comfort. As parents, we must explain to our children about socially acceptable behaviour, whilst acknowledging that touching these areas gives them pleasure. It is important not to incite shame but to give guidance about appropriate times and places, so the child can continue to enjoy doing it. This can also be part of a wider conversation with our children about who can touch their bodies, and more specifically their genitals, and how to talk about inappropriate touching by other people. Looking at and touching our genitals is the first step towards understanding our bodies.

As a sex therapist, within minutes of meeting an individual or couple, I will ask the most personal questions about what they do sexually and how their bodies respond. How well do they know their own bodies?

When I am working with a woman, I will ask about periods and what sanitary protection she uses. Some will be comfortable with tampons, others not. Some men are happy to talk about their erections and masturbation; others find it difficult. Without generalising too much, I find those patients who are more comfortable with their bodies generally have fewer inhibitions around sex and tend to enjoy it more. They are more open-minded and willing to experiment with new things. Broadening one's sexual repertoire is vital to keep sex alive, and to nurture what Esther Perel has described as "erotic intelligence", and we will consider this in the next chapter.

Our sexual script

Some couples have difficulties with what I describe as the "sexual script" that they have metaphorically written for themselves. This is the perception they have, often unconsciously, about how they are going to behave sexually and what this might include. A rigid sexual script can be debilitating. If sexual intimacy does not go according to plan, or their partner has a different sexual script, then there will be challenges for the couple or individual. Our sexual script will be influenced by all sorts of things. The way our parents or main caregivers talked about sex or indeed did not talk about it; our religious beliefs and those of our parents – all these will impact how we view sex and intimacy. Is it something to be celebrated or hidden? Our sexual script will be influenced by the way we have felt about our bodies through childhood and into adolescence and puberty. It will be influenced by first sexual experiences, both positive and negative.

Sometimes I will work with patients who grew up in conservative religious families – Christian, Muslim, Hindu, Jewish or Sikh. Even if they no longer practise this faith, they can still be carrying the messages passed down to them from others: their parents, grandparents, religious leaders, and teachers. All these voices will impact how they believe they should behave sexually, the sexual script they have constructed for themselves. Sometimes it is positive but more often than not it is constraining. These scripts might include messages such as "You must not enjoy yourself" or "Nice girls do not instigate sex" or "Sex is only for procreation." Maybe they might warn "Don't suggest new things" or state "Orgasms are just for men" and "Sex will be really painful", even "It is not okay to touch your own body."

It can be really difficult to throw off these scripts and act from a place of choice and autonomy. As we enter marriage, we may believe these scripts will magically disappear but very often they do not. A number of couples I have worked with have said they assumed that once they were married, they would fall into a free-flowing sexual relationship, full of sexual desire, especially if they had waited until marriage to have sex. Often they are disappointed and find it is not the case. The long-held messages of "Do not…" and "You must not…" are hard to erase.

We cannot change our pasts, but if we can find a way to talk about these messages with our spouse, then we can start to abandon our individual sexual script and forge a joint one full of new possibilities. This can take time. When I am working with a couple, I will ask them to tell me in detail how they believe sexual behaviour with their partner should work. This can be such a helpful exercise, highlighting unconscious views or stereotypes that we hold without realising it. For example, a woman might say: "Obviously my husband would be the one to initiate sex." I might then question why this is "obvious" and they will reply: "That's what happens in films" or "That is what my mother said should happen; a woman should never initiate sex." Perhaps this woman is married to a man who subconsciously holds the belief that a woman should initiate sex. Maybe he grew up in a family with a very dominant pushy father, and he believes he must never appear aggressive, and this in his mind might include initiating sex.

Having these conversations out in the open can help couples to see how they may have got into patterns of behaviour that are not working well for them, or behaviours that are restricting or confusing. Some couples might have to go through the motions of acting out their new scripts, even if this takes them out of their comfort zone. Couples can feel shy, inhibited or disingenuous, but I encourage them to verbalise this: "I feel really uncomfortable telling you I want sex tonight but I do" or "I would really like to try oral sex, even though part of me is deeply uncomfortable admitting this."

This sort of exposing revelations about ourselves can seem risky, making us feel very vulnerable. What if my spouse reinforces the very thing I have grown up believing? Maybe a woman plucks up the courage to instigate sex with her husband, only to be rebuffed: "I'm not comfortable with you being so sexually forward; I have always believed that it is the man's job to instigate sex." This kind of risk-taking can, however, also create huge intimacy with our partner. As an intimate team, in a spirit of respect and kindness, the couple can start to talk about letting go of constraining unhelpful beliefs and create a new sexual script together. This will undoubtedly have the tensions, fears, expectancy, and hope of something new and completely unique to that couple, woven into it.

Sex for the first time: realistic expectations

I regularly work with couples who for religious or cultural reasons have waited until their wedding night to have sexual intercourse. Some have had sexual contact and foreplay with their partners during their courtship but have waited to their wedding night to have full intercourse. Other couples have very little or no previous sexual experience prior to their wedding night. Whether a couple has previous sexual experience or not, an overarching theme for many is that sex on their wedding night will be amazing. Often these beliefs are shaped by scenes from films or romantic novels. In these scenes the couple passionately embrace, there is little, or no, foreplay, and the man seamlessly and effortlessly inserts his penis in the woman's vagina. After no time at all the two simultaneously orgasm and fall back into each other's arms, as the stars align, and the earth moves!

For some couples it may not be quite like this scenario, but the wedding night is still very special. Everything works as it should and the experience is positive and really unifying. For many couples, though, it takes time for penetrative sex not only to feel comfortable and pleasurable, but for the couple to feel confident knowing what to do during foreplay and intercourse. If you have had little or no sexual contact with your spouse prior to the wedding night, you may also find it takes some time to feel fully comfortable being naked in front of them.

It may be that you have never had sexual intercourse and you are reading this book to deepen your understanding of what sexual intimacy might involve and how this can be nurtured in your forthcoming marriage. Or you may have had previous sexual experience in past relationships, but you have not had sex with your current partner and you are waiting until your wedding night. This is wonderful and there is no doubt that the fact that you are waiting creates an exciting anticipation. I would encourage you to talk with your fiancé/fiancée about your hopes and fears for your wedding night.

It is important to be realistic. Both of you will probably be very tired from the excitement of the day. For the couple getting married, a wedding day is a day like no other. You probably did not have enough sleep in the run-up to the wedding. You may have eaten very little on the day and consumed alcohol. You are very likely to be in a hotel for your wedding night, in unfamiliar circumstances.

The physical act of intercourse can also be challenging as our bodies get used to what we are expecting them to do. Penetrative sex for women initially can be uncomfortable and, for some women, quite painful. Some women will notice a small amount of blood from their vagina the first time or couple of times they make love. This is completely normal. It may come from a slight graze in the introitus (the vaginal opening) or it could be from the hymen. This is a thin membrane of skin that partially covers the vagina. In some women this can be broken during sexual intercourse. For many women the hymen has already torn, without their realising it, perhaps because they have used tampons or through physical exercise, dance, gymnastics, etc.

I have worked with a couple of women who have grown up in families where the female members of the family – mother, sisters, aunts, grandmothers – have told the women horror stories about how painful sexual intercourse will be and that they will bleed a lot. This has terrified the women and set up unhelpful fears. When I have come to the end of the work with these women, and they have been able to have full sexual intercourse, I have asked them what they would tell any daughters they might have in the future, about sex. It has heartened me when they have said they would simply say: "It takes a little bit of time to know what to do and to gain confidence, but it is nothing like the horror stories I was told."

Many couples will say it took a number of attempts before they were able to fully insert the penis into the vagina, because the woman tenses up and the pelvic muscles tighten. Ensuring that the couple have had adequate foreplay so that the woman is sufficiently sexually aroused is really important. Using lots of vaginal lubrication will also help.

Sex for the first time for the man can also be challenging. The temptation for him can be to want to have penetrative intercourse as soon as he has a full erection, and this can take some navigation if the woman is not ready. Sometimes a man will want to rush to intercourse through fear of losing his erection or ejaculating too quickly. Some men feel so intensely aroused they ejaculate before they have penetrated their partner, and this can be disappointing for both. Couples often find that if they attempt sex again after a period of time (this is called the refractory period and can be as quick as fifteen minutes in a young man and gets progressively longer as he ages), the intensity of the arousal is less, and the couple are able to achieve intercourse successfully.

It can, therefore, be a good idea for both partners if you have some idea of your own bodies before you first make love, and there are some self-focusing exercises below that can help with this. (See page 53).

If you find you are experiencing difficulties, then do not lose hope. Often these will resolve quickly and without any formal intervention, by following the self-help strategies laid out in the various chapters. If the problem persists, and you have seen no improvements after three months, then seek help quickly so that you do not find yourself avoiding sexual intimacy or find that this negatively affects the relationship.

How we treat our spouse when they are struggling sexually can have such a positive or negative impact on how they feel about themselves, about us, and on our ability, as a couple, to get over the difficulty. I have worked with men and women whose partners have been so overwhelmed by disappointment when sex has not gone as they hoped that they lashed out with very hurtful words. It is so important that we are kind and patient with our partners. Remember you are a team and you are on the same side.

How do we get to know our bodies?

Regardless of whether we have a faith or not, most of us agree our bodies are amazingly constructed. If we have a faith, we will believe our bodies have been intricately designed by God and did not simply occur by chance. They are designed to be functional, and to experience pleasure through many different senses. For instance, the only function of the clitoris is to stimulate feelings of pleasure in the woman (see drawing on page 54). God has created us to enjoy life through sight, sound, touch, smell, and taste. We have many ways of responding to the world around us, including our minds, a powerful tool for creating imagination and fantasy.

Children in particular are able to instinctively tune in to their senses, in the moment. That is why children can be so refreshing to be around. "Look at that ladybird!" "Smell that lovely warm bread!" "This blanket feels all soft and cuddly." "This cabbage tastes horrible!" Adults tend to dampen down their senses and live much of their lives in their heads. If we recognise that, to enjoy sex, we need to fully "inhabit" our bodies and accept sexual intimacy will involve almost all of our senses, then we can appreciate the need to awaken these.

The process of desire may start in our head, but it can be heightened when it moves from our head to our body. To enjoy sex, we need to be sexually aroused. As we respond to the feelings of arousal, so we fuel it, and the peak of arousal, for many, is orgasm. So, in order to be in the moment, we must be fully aware of what we are feeling physically. If that is currently a struggle, there are lots of ways of learning to do it better. It would be too big a step to start with sex itself, so initially I encourage patients to practise unthreatening non-sexual *sensual* exercises. They often feel frustrated at this, wanting to get on to sexual intercourse, but this preparatory work is essential.

When performing these exercises, there are no right or wrong outcomes. Just be aware of and curious about your responses.

Sensual exercises (for men and women)

Having a shower or bath

Start with buying shower gel or bath oil you really like, one which sparks a positive response of joy in you. It could be the smell you like, the texture, or the beautifully designed bottle. Some people can struggle even to do this; maybe they do not know what they like. But sex is about pleasure, being indulgent; enjoying your body, enjoying your partner's body, and giving each other pleasure.

When you take the first shower using your new shower gel, give yourself enough time not to rush. When you step into the shower, how do you feel when the water touches your skin? Is it too hot, too cold? Is the water forceful or light? What does the water taste like? As you use your new product, think about how the smell makes you feel. What does it feel like to run your hands over your arms, legs, and chest?

Using body lotion

As with the shower gel, find something with a smell and texture you like. When you have plenty of time, apply it gently and carefully to your whole body. Take time to notice the parts of your body that perhaps you ignore. What feelings does this evoke in you?

If you have found doing these exercises more difficult than you expected, or they have brought up painful feelings, then perhaps stop doing them. If I am working with someone who has experienced sexual abuse, I begin with these non-threatening exercises as a way to encourage the person to try to connect the thoughts in their heads with the sensations in their bodies. Victims of sexual abuse will often say they have learnt ways to disengage what they are thinking in their heads from what has been done to their bodies. This makes complete sense when we think about the sort of survival mechanisms that a child, for example, would have found necessary if they were being abused. They won't, however, serve the individual well in adulthood, when they want to enjoy sexual intimacy with a partner. Maybe these exercises have uncovered issues for you that you were not aware of. Perhaps considering a therapist at this point might be a good idea. You could consider taking this experience to therapy as a good starting point and something to explore. You can always revisit these exercises at a later date.

Going for a walk

Choose somewhere you want to explore. Focus on how your body responds to the air on your face. Is it cold and jarring or warm and soothing? How does it feel when you charge up a hill? Are your lungs bursting and your legs pounding? How does it feel to run down a hill – scary, exhilarating? What can you see and smell?

Dancing

I worked with a wonderful clinical supervisor who always encouraged his clients to talk about what dancing was like for them, because he felt it often represented what sex can feel like for some people. When you dance, do you feel very self-conscious, not quite sure where to put your limbs and how to move in time with the music? Or can you freely enjoy the experience? Are you preoccupied with getting the steps right? Or do you not care what others think?

Cooking

Cooking has the potential to evoke all our senses. So, set some time aside, choose a new recipe that interests you, and buy all the ingredients, maybe in a market, where you can feel, smell, and touch the produce. Take your time to enjoy the whole process and be aware of what your senses are telling you, from the shopping through to the eating. You might enjoy doing this with your partner and talking about what you are both experiencing. I'm not suggesting you try to make this exercise sexual in any way; this is about being "in the moment" in yourself and with the other person.

Have a massage

If you feel ambivalent about being touched, how about having a massage? You may love it, you may not: both can be helpful in understanding your own reactions. How did you feel about your body? How did you experience the room? Was it a pleasing sensual experience, or did you feel awkward?

Mindfulness

Some people find it really difficult to relax and to allow themselves to be "in the moment." If you have struggled with the idea of these exercises, then you might want to try mindfulness. This exercise involves being fully aware of the moment you are in, your breathing, how your various body parts feel, and allowing other distractions to fade. It can be a very helpful way to relax and is being used increasingly in healthcare settings and therapy. There is also evidence that it can be effective when combined with sex therapy.[1] See Appendix 4 for more information.

All these exercises are good starting points, helping you to attune to your body and what you are experiencing. Later in the chapter I am going to discuss ways we can get to know our bodies more intimately, but before I do, it is worth considering the male and female arousal models because an understanding of these can be very helpful.

Sexual desire / arousal models

Over the years, couples regularly say some of the most useful information I have given them is an understanding of the different ways in which men and women experience sexual desire and sexual arousal. So here is an overview of two of the popular sexual desire/arousal models I discuss with my patients, because research suggests there are significant differences in the way men and women function in relation to sexual desire/arousal.

William Masters and Virginia Johnson pioneered research into the nature of human sexual response and the diagnosis and treatment of sexual disorders and dysfunctions, from 1957 until the 1990s. They jointly wrote the classic text, *Human Sexual Response*, published in 1966.[2] This was a best-seller, and much of my training as a psychosexual therapist was based on their work and the knowledge we have today about the human sexual response cycle. The response cycle identifies four distinct phases:

1. excitement phase, including desire and arousal
2. plateau phase, at full arousal, but not orgasm
3. orgasm
4. resolution, where the body returns to its normal state

Masters and Johnson suggest that one moves through the four linear stages from desire to resolution.

Masters and Johnson's Sexual Response Model

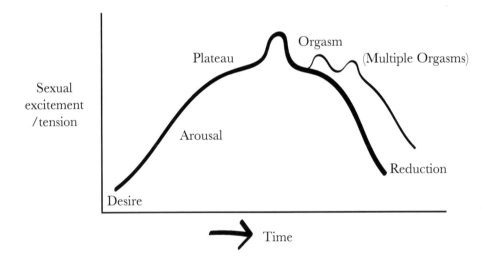

Another researcher, Rosemary Basson,[3] has looked more recently at the female response cycle, and she suggests men and women do not necessarily follow the linear model identified by Masters and Johnson. She argues that, unlike men, women have less spontaneous sexual desire and are often in sexual "neutral." This does not mean that they do not want sex, but it is not necessarily at the forefront of their minds.

Female Sexual Response Cycle

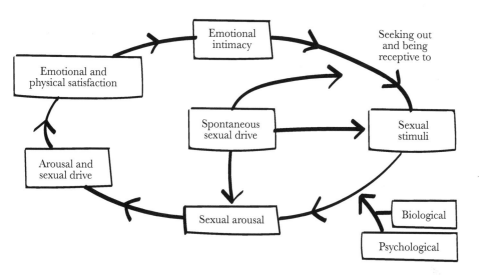

Basson suggests that for women, sexual desire is actually triggered if two important factors are present. Firstly, she suggests a woman is more likely to be able to switch from neutral to sexually interested if she is feeling psychologically connected to her partner and positive about the relationship. Basson argues that if a woman is unhappy, feels unheard, or is dissatisfied with the relationship, this can directly affect her willingness to engage in sex, and that is why effective communication is so important. If there is a fundamental dissatisfaction within the relationship, then both parties need to address this before the sexual difficulties can be adequately addressed.

Secondly, the woman often needs to be sexually aroused through touch, talking or physical contact for the sexual desire to follow. At this point, we need to understand the physical responses in men and women when we talk about sexual arousal. What do we mean by this term and why is it identified as such an important factor in Rosemary Basson's model?

Arousal/excitement

When we talk about arousal it means a physical response or excitement, usually as a result of feeling sexual desire. Arousal happens as your body prepares itself for, and responds to, sexual stimulus.

Men

In a man, the first sign is often an erection. This is produced when the brain sends messages to release nitric oxide from nerve endings in the penis. The chemical dilates the blood vessels, allowing the penis to fill with blood. This in turn constricts the veins that allow blood to leave the area, leading to the enlargement and hardening of the penis. Other signs of arousal for a man may include flushing of the skin, breathing more heavily, and feeling tense and sweaty. As arousal builds, the testicles swell slightly, the scrotum tightens, and drops of liquid (pre-cum) may start to seep from the end of the penis.

If arousal continues and increases, seminal fluid builds up in the prostate gland until the prostate, seminal vesicles, and vas deferens begin to contract and expel the seminal fluid. This is called emission and may be felt as warmth or as sharp, intensely pleasurable contractions involving the pelvic floor muscles, anal sphincter, rectum, perineum, and genitals. Once this has happened, the man has reached a point of no return (or "ejaculatory inevitability") after which he will ejaculate, whatever happens. Once he has reached this point, a man experiences a warm rush of fluid or a shooting sensation as the semen travels through the urethra and is expelled. The amount of fluid ejaculated can vary in quantity but is usually about a teaspoonful. If a man has not had a vasectomy, the fluid contains millions of sperms (not visible to the naked eye). If he has had a vasectomy, he will still ejaculate seminal fluid, but it will not contain the sperm. Either way, the fluid is perfectly clean and hygienic.

Usually, as the man ejaculates, he also experiences an orgasm: an intensely pleasurable build-up and release of tension, usually followed by a feeling of well-being and calm. Some men, for physical or psychological reasons, ejaculate but experience no sensation of orgasm. Some men experience the sensation of an orgasm but do not ejaculate, or ejaculate inwardly into the bladder. This is called "retrograde ejaculation" and results in cloudy urine following orgasm, which is harmless. Some men find a change in their ejaculatory process difficult and I discuss this in more detail in chapters 9 and 10, on early and delayed ejaculation/orgasmic disorders in men.

Women

Arousal in women is not as obvious, and some women may not be aware of the changes taking place. Signs can include flushing of the skin, increased genital and breast sensitivity, nipples hardening, the clitoris swelling and becoming erect, wetness or lubrication (often hidden inside the vagina), and a sense of swelling, warmth or tingling in the vulva and vagina. In addition, the uterus and cervix are pulled upwards and the innermost part of the vagina expands by 2–3cm as arousal increases.

If arousal continues and builds, then a woman will often reach the point of orgasm. Many women experience orgasm as the same increase in tension as men, followed by a pleasurable compelling release, lasting approximately five to fifteen seconds. This may be experienced as waves rushing throughout the body, especially in the genital area. Some women will also be aware of contractions of the muscles surrounding the vagina. Climax is often followed by a feeling of well-being and tranquillity, as it is for men. Not all women experience orgasms, and most will do so only if the sexual activity has included stimulation of the clitoris by their partner's finger or tongue, their own finger, a vibrator or being in sexual positions where the clitoris is stimulated either directly or indirectly by the penis during thrusting. Some women can experience more than one orgasm, and these are called multiple orgasms, if stimulation continues. Both men and women often notice their orgasms are more intense if they have enjoyed adequate foreplay prior to intercourse.

It's worth remembering not all orgasms are earth-moving events. Orgasms and the process to reach orgasm involve the whole body, and therefore simple things like how tired you are, how much alcohol you have consumed, your general mood, as well as how aroused you are feeling, will all have an impact on the intensity of the experience.

Men and women

For men and women, arousal often comes in waves, with increasing and decreasing erections and vulval/vaginal responses. This is perfectly normal. The sexual response cycle involves moment by moment feedback between the body, the mind, and the emotions, which means the levels of arousal will wax and wane. The secret is to enjoy this, instead of worrying about it. When we start to worry about how our bodies are responding, we create a pattern of performance anxiety which can be difficult to break.

It is important for couples to remember that when a man has an erection, this does not mean he is necessarily ready for penetrative sex straightaway. Some men, if they are not adequately stimulated through foreplay, may be able to maintain their erection but will have difficulty reaching orgasm through penetrative intercourse. This will be increasingly common as a man gets older. Many older men need more "hands on" stimulation prior to sexual intercourse. The same applies to women. The longer the arousal phase goes on, the more likely a woman is to be ready for penetration, and the more comfortable this will be. Rushing into penetrative sex too early can often lead to discomfort for the woman, or

HOW OUR BODIES WORK

erectile problems for the man, both of which will impact their enjoyment. I talk more about this in Chapters 10 and 11.

Resolution

This is the period when the body settles down, and both partners often feel pleasantly relaxed. After an orgasm, endorphins are released into the body by the brain. These hormones are also released after exercise and create a sense of calm and well-being. Following the orgasm, the blood flows out of the penis, which returns to its usual size and shape. For a woman, the feeling of fullness and congestion in her pelvis slowly subsides.

How to know your body intimately: a few words

When people see me about the sex-related problems they are having, I advise them first of all to get comfortable touching their own bodies. They can do this by practising a number of self-focusing exercises at home; then they come back and we talk about those experiences.

It is important to differentiate self-focusing exercises from masturbation, because some Christians are uncomfortable with the thought of masturbation and it does not sit comfortably with their beliefs. In the Muslim faith, masturbation is forbidden but self-focusing exercises are permitted, if it is felt that these will help the man or woman overcome a sexual problem so that they can be fully sexual with their spouse. This is such a helpful approach. Masturbation is self-stimulation for one's own personal sexual pleasure. Self-focused exercises have a very different focus, helping the individual feel fully connected with their bodies and intricately in tune with the bodily sensations they are experiencing. Sometimes these will be highly pleasurable and orgasm may occur. If so, that is fine, but it is not the aim.

53

How to know your body intimately – for women

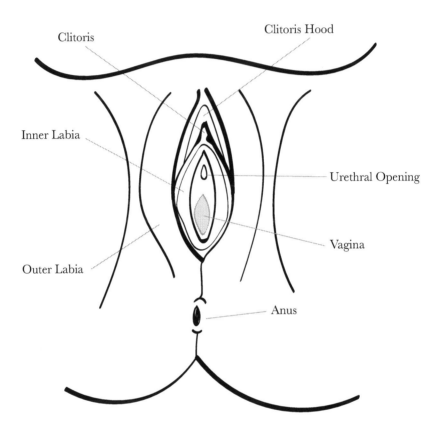

Some women know very little about the female anatomy, particularly female genitals. Unless a woman purposefully chooses to look at her own vulva (the area that can be seen externally), using a mirror, it remains unseen. But if a woman wants to be sexually intimate with her partner, she needs to understand what is happening and take a sense of ownership over this so she does not feel as though it is happening to someone else.

If you are a woman, and want to learn more, then have a bath or shower so that you are warm and relaxed and, once dry, get into a comfortable position. This could be lying on the bed propped up with cushions, crouching down on the floor or standing with one leg up on a step or table. Get a fairly large hand-held mirror (you can get these from most chemists) and look at your vulva.

If you find this difficult, it may be that you have heard the vaginal area being described in a shameful or derogatory way. Perhaps you were discouraged as a child from touching your genitals or told they were dirty. But looking at our genitals, appreciating that they are a fundamental part of our design and being proud of them, is an important first step for many women. If you are a Christian, it might be comforting to think about how God designed us:

So God created mankind in his own image, in the image of God
he created them; male and female he created them

Genesis 1:27

Everything that God has designed is good. It is also important to remember that if you want to enjoy your spouse touching you to sexually arouse you, it is very helpful for him if you can articulate how and where you like to be touched.

Once you are comfortable looking at your genitals, you might like to try some exercises where you experiment touching the vulva and then inserting a finger into your vagina. Again, take some time when you will not be interrupted and feel warm and relaxed. It can be helpful to lie on the bed or an area where you can comfortably recline. Lying with your legs apart, you may want to start touching other areas of your body before you focus on the genital area. This may include your breasts, thighs or any area that you enjoy touching. When you feel suitably relaxed, apply some vaginal lubricant to your fingers to ensure, when you touch your genital area, it is smooth and there is no friction. (There is more information in the next chapter on vaginal lubrication.)

Let your fingers explore the area usually covered by pubic hair, then move down to touch the outer lips (labia majora). What does this feel like? Move your fingers all over this area and take some time to notice particular areas that are sensitive, and areas you enjoy touching. Be aware of areas that perhaps you do not feel are as pleasurable to touch. You can then move on to touching the inner lips of the vulva (labia minora). You may like to move your fingers up to touch your clitoris. The clitoris is covered by a "hood" and for most women this will feel very sensitive to the touch. You may like to gently retract this to see what it feels like to touch the clitoris directly.

Once you have done this you may like to apply some more lubrication and touch the entrance to your vagina. This is called the introitus. Then try inserting your finger into your vagina. This may be just your fingertip or you may feel comfortable and relaxed enough to insert more or your entire finger. What can you feel? A common misconception is that the vagina is a hollow channel; it is actually made up of muscles that touch and when you insert your finger you may feel them move apart. If you have been able to insert your finger you might like to try clenching your pelvic floor muscles (these are the muscles you tense to stop yourself urinating mid-flow). These are also the muscles that contract for some women during orgasm.

The G-Spot

There is much debate about whether the G-Spot exists. The G-Spot is described as a lump that can be felt on the wall of the vagina towards the stomach, about one to two inches inside the introitus. You might like to see if you can feel this lump for yourself. Given there is so much debate amongst clinicians about whether it exists or, if so, what its role is in sexual arousal and orgasm, I am not going to focus on it in any more detail in this book.

You may notice you are beginning to feel sexually aroused, as you touch your body, particularly your vulval area and vagina. You may like to increase the intensity or stimulation around your clitoral area and, for some, this may lead to an orgasm. This is great because it is helpful information to take back to your partner about how and where you enjoy being touched. Remember it is quite difficult to instruct your partner about what you like and how you like it, if you don't actually know yourself. The more information you have, the better.

The idea of doing these self-exploratory exercises is to encourage you to start to get comfortable with looking at and touching your body, if you haven't done so before. In the next chapter I discuss some of the benefits of using a vibrator with your spouse, which many women find helpful, particularly for clitoral stimulation.

How to know your body intimately for men

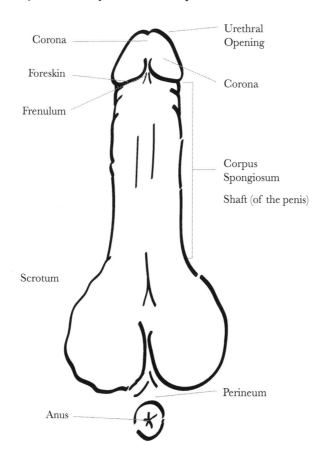

In my practice I also meet men who are not necessarily very familiar with how their bodies respond. We can wrongly assume that because boys are more likely to have communal showers at school, there will be an ease with being naked, and we can also wrongly assume that all adolescent boys masturbate and therefore understand how their genitals and bodies respond to touch. I regularly meet men who will say that they developed very subtle ways of touching themselves or rubbing themselves to get aroused or masturbate that are unique to them. Sometimes this is because they went to a boarding school and they were aware of others in close proximity. It might be because they grew up in a house with no privacy, so they had to learn to do this subtly and quickly.

Having a very specific technique to get aroused can be as limiting as having no knowledge about one's arousal. When we bring our experiences into a sexual relationship with another person, it may be very hard for our partner to replicate these very specific ways of touching, which means that neither partner may be able to fully relax and enjoy the moment. Either we don't know what to expect or we have very rigid ways of how we like to be touched.

You might like to try these self-focused exercises. While having a bath or shower, touch your penis and scrotal area, in an intentional way: the idea is to fully connect with what touching it feels like. Use your hand and the sensation of the water to experiment with soft touching, light touching, slow touching. Engage in what you are experiencing. You may feel aroused and you can experiment with experiencing this sensation and then letting it pass. You may want to repeat this exercise a couple of times to the point of ejaculation.

In the following chapter, I give some more exercises for men and women to build on the sensually focused exercises outlined in this chapter. These exercises move on from sensual touching and focus more on a sexual growth programme, helping us to understand how we experience pleasure and how this increases sexual arousal.

Does size matter?

In men

Sometimes I get asked about the importance of size in relation to a man's penis. A number of studies have been done looking at average penis length, both placid and erect. Professor Kevan Wylie conducted a study based on the results of an internet-based survey of more than 50,000 men and women, and this revealed that 45 percent of men would like a larger penis. However, he found 85 percent of women were satisfied with their partner's penis size.[4]

Professor Wylie's research has shown that men's concern over the size of their penis is entirely unnecessary, and that, when it comes to sex, women are much more interested in whether men are romantic, gentle and attuned to their partner's sexual needs and desire.

There is an extremely rare condition called micropenis. It is diagnosed in infanthood. The flaccid length of a boy's penis is usually under 4cm at birth and changes very little until puberty, when there is marked growth. In micropenis, the stretched penile length for a new-born infant is less than 1.9cm.[5] In these cases, surgical intervention will be needed later in life.

In women

Sometimes I get asked whether the size of the vagina matters, especially if sex is painful (dyspareunia). Women's vaginas and vulval areas are all unique and vary in size, shape, and colour. The vagina is very elastic and designed to accommodate a man's penis and the birth of a baby. During sex we know that the size of the vagina increases by about 2–3cm when the woman is sexually aroused, and this is part of God's design to get the body ready for penetrative intercourse. This is another reason why adequate foreplay is important, prior to penetrative intercourse.

Body dysmorphic disorder

Body dysmorphic disorder (BDD) or body dysmorphia is a mental health condition where a person spends a lot of time worrying about flaws in their appearance. These flaws are often unnoticeable to others. I have worked with patients anxious about their breasts or genitals. Women worry about the size and shape of their labia; men worry about the size or shape of their penis. The anxiety can become an all-consuming preoccupation. The person starts to believe a particular body part is the source of all their unhappiness or anxiety and if they can get this surgically altered, then all their problems will disappear. In fact, they often then become fixated with another body part, and the underlying anxiety and self-esteem issues are never fully addressed.

BDD is a mental health condition and will usually be addressed by the mental health services. If you feel fixated on a belief about a part of your body and this is impacting your ability to function either sexually or more widely in your everyday life, then I would encourage you to see your GP. They can firstly examine you and hopefully reassure you, but also refer you for some specialist help, if necessary. For more information on BDD please see:
www.nhs.uk/conditions/body-dysmorphia

Conclusion

As I come to the end of this chapter I am aware that I have covered a lot of ground: knowing our bodies, what typically happens during the sexual arousal circuit, and exercises to increase sensual awareness. For some readers, these concepts can be challenging or abstract, particularly the need to appreciate our bodies as sensual creations. But if we can embrace ourselves as sensual beings first, we are much better placed to enjoy and understand our sexual responses and then share them with our partner.

This might have stirred up some thoughts for discussion. Perhaps it has unsettled you or brought out some difficult emotions. I have talked about the varying significance sex can hold for us. This may pose challenges about the need to rethink sexual intimacy as a positive force given to us by a loving God. If I am working with someone who has experienced sexual abuse or sexual trauma, I am acutely aware that they may face additional challenges in needing to reframe the way they think about their bodies and sexual intimacy. This can be very painful but I believe it is possible, with the support of a loving partner and, in some cases, professional help. If this applies to you, specific information in Appendix 5 may help, as may Chapter 5.

References

1. Mize, S. (2015) A review of mindfulness-based Sex therapy interventions for sexual desire and arousal difficulties: from research to practice. *Current Sexual Health Reports*, 7(2), 89–97.

2. W.H. Masters and V.E. Johnson, *Human Sexual Response*, (New York: Bantam Books, 1966).

3. Basson, R. (2000) The female sexual response: a different model. *Journal of Sex and Marital Therapy*, 26, 51–65.

4. Wylie, K. Eardley, I. (2007) Penile size and the 'small penis syndrome', *British Journal of Urology International*, 99, 1449-1455.

5. Wiygul, J. Palmer, L. (2011) Micropenis. *The Scientific World Journal*, 11, 1462–69.

CHAPTER THREE

With My Body I Honour You: How to Nurture Lifelong Desire and Good Sexual Intimacy

Let him kiss me with the kisses of his mouth —
for your love is more delightful than wine.

Song of Songs 1:2

I n 2016 I was interviewed along with a couple of other sex and relationship therapists for a piece in the *Guardian* newspaper (23 July 2016) on "Sex and the long term lover." I felt it was wonderful to see sex in the committed relationship celebrated in this way, as so much of the media tends to focus on sex in the early whirlwind phase of a new relationship. If you think about the sex scenes you may have seen in films, many will be focused around passion and lust. The couple are having fast, often vigorous sex, perhaps in challenging acrobatic positions. This can leave the audience wondering if this is how all other couples make love, because it is not how they do it. This comparison can then create some very unhelpful expectations.

The sex we are presented with on-screen is rarely sexual intimacy between committed couples, nor are they likely to be over the age of fifty – at least, the woman isn't. It is unusual to see situations where the sex does not work, but if, for instance, the man loses his erection, this will be portrayed negatively, not as something that can be addressed positively. We are rarely shown sex between couples who are trying for a baby and struggling to find the enthusiasm to do so. Nor do we see sex scenes where the woman is recovering from a mastectomy and cannot bring herself to be naked in front of her husband of thirty years, or sex where the woman is finding it painful and the couple need to stop to apply lubrication.

So all we are shown is sex in the spring or summer seasons – free-flowing, spontaneous, and working well. If we find ourselves in the autumn or winter seasons of sex, we can be bewildered. Surely nobody else faces these difficulties? We must be abnormal. Yet, in all my experience of working with hundreds of couples, few have the kind of sex we see on screen. Most sex takes place in bed, at the end of the day, with a couple who are tired, and where one would often rather be going to sleep.

Being intentional

If we really want to enjoy sex, we have to be intentional about what we are doing and fully engaged in the moment. This can be a real challenge. We are used to living our lives in our heads and so can be disconnected from our bodies. Think how often we ignore what our bodies are telling us: "Have a rest", "Go to the loo", "Have a drink." We are so preoccupied, we push these messages aside and press on with what we are doing. Learning to listen to our bodies is crucial if we want to enjoy sex. We need to focus on the tiniest of physical sensations. We need to stay engaged to recognise arousal, to savour it. If we are distracted and not fully aware of what is happening in our bodies, then we won't be able to do this.

What is erotic intelligence?

Another key issue in creating an intimate team is erotic intelligence, and there is a lot more about this in sex therapist Esther Perel's book, *Mating in Captivity*.[1] At the heart of the concept is a rejection of the idea that sex should be spontaneous. Many couples shrink from the idea of timetabling sex because they associate this with a sense of obligation and this feels like hard work – the very thing in their minds sex shouldn't be. However being intentional about sex and when this will happen is essential to taking responsibility for our own sexual needs and ensuring that sexual intimacy is a regular part of our relationship.

Timetabling

So how can we take Esther Perel's idea of being intentional and put it into practice? Many sex therapists suggest couples should structure sexual intimacy into a normal week, and this can be as useful for those couples who are having difficulties as for those who are not. Just as "date nights" can give a couple planned time together, so too planning a time for sexual intimacy can work well. In fact, this idea is gaining interest in the general media, which recognises it can be a helpful tool for couples who are juggling lots of commitments and have very little time to devote to sexual intimacy. If a couple is not having much sex and wants this to change, however much they might dislike the idea of planning intimacy, this is the only way of ensuring progress in many cases. Very simply, if we want a different outcome, we have to act differently.

The timetabling approach works best for busy couples who are strong intimate teams with no real sexual problems. To judge whether this technique might be helpful for you, consider what sex is like when you are away on holiday, without the usual pressures of life. Do you naturally fall back into a relaxed routine of making love, or is it strained and formulaic? If you feel confident that a holiday would quickly reignite the sexual side of your relationship, then probably the lack of sex in everyday life is down to the pressures of life. Like going to the gym or exercising generally, if it isn't in the diary, it won't happen, even though we know it will benefit us. Exercise – and sex – both produce endorphins which help us to feel calm and lift our spirits. Many couples who start having sex after long periods of little or no intimacy will say: "It was really nice and we wonder why we don't do it more often."

How do we use the timetabling model?

So how do you timetable sexual intimacy into your calendar? You start, as a couple, by discussing when you each most prefer sex. Morning? Evening? When the children are definitely asleep? What if you have teenagers? Do you have a proper lock on your bedroom door? You may need to compromise; you may need to be creative. Some couples have never considered engineering sexual intimacy into a weekend afternoon when both of them feel a little more rested than on a weekday night. It can be difficult to consider timetabling something you will enjoy if you believe that sex is simply for procreation, or your needs are not as important as those of your children.

Timetabling can also create a sense of anticipation which often fuels desire. If a couple has arranged to have a date night every week devoted to enjoying each other, this is a good prelude. It can also work well for couples where one wants sex a lot more than the other. The person who wants less sex often feels their partner is being "predatory" and that creates more of a problem. The more a person feels pursued, the more they want to retreat, and so the other partner feels increasingly rejected.

Timetabling can be a constructive way to end this destructive dynamic. If the couple can make a binding agreement to, say, having sex once a week, then there will be no pressure on the more reluctant partner to perform beyond that. Meanwhile, the keen partner will know their needs will be met at least that often. It is worth emphasising here that the agreement must be binding (unless there is a valid reason why it cannot be upheld), because this approach works on trust from both partners and an understanding that both partners have a vested interest in adhering to the agreement.

If you want to try this approach, do think through any challenges you may meet. Remember you are stepping out in faith, and pray about the new strategy. Ask God for wisdom and insight, help and guidance. Timetabling only works if low desire is not a fundamental problem. If both spouses feel mutual attraction, the relationship is strong, and both can get sexually aroused, then timetabling can help, especially if tiredness or stress are issues. But if one partner has lost all sexual desire, this may require a sex therapist and further intervention.

Sensate focus exercises

For couples that are experiencing sexual difficulties or who have not had close physical or sexual contact for some time, sensate focus exercises can be a very helpful way of encouraging physical closeness and sexual intimacy. This programme is a series of homework exercises completed by the couple at home, and originally designed by researchers and sex therapists Masters and Johnson. They are designed so couples first become more comfortable and confident with physical contact and then, over time, move on to sexual intimacy including, in most cases, sexual intercourse. You don't need to be seeing a sex therapist in order to try them, but some couples might find such extra support helpful.

Before embarking on the exercises, ask yourselves the following questions:

- Have either of you experienced any form of sexual trauma or sex abuse?

- Is the lack of physical or sexual contact creating tension in the marriage?

✐ Is the thought of re-engaging in intimate touching causing either of you high levels of distress, anxiety or depression?

✐ Has the marriage become "sexless", i.e. you have stopped engaging in any form of sexual intimacy completely?

If you answer "Yes" to any of these questions, then I suggest that you find a therapist. If you didn't, then I suggest you have a go at the programme and consider finding a therapist if you struggle with the exercises. These exercises can expose underlying tensions in a marriage that have not been addressed before, and you will need to openly and sensitively recognise these challenges and work towards finding your own solutions.

Non-genital sensate focus

Setting the scene/ground rules

The key to succeeding with this approach is to try to abstain from sexual intercourse or any touching of genital areas (breasts, nipples, penis, vagina, testicles or clitoris) in the early sessions, while you are re-establishing close physical contact. This ensures both partners know what to expect, and it reduces performance anxiety, which is often heightened for couples who are experiencing sexual difficulties. And if a couple have not been physically close for some time, it allows them to get used to feeling so, without the added pressure of being sexual at this stage. This approach can also be a helpful tool at other points in marriage where the couple want to maintain physical intimacy but are not able to engage in full intercourse or even foreplay. This might include recovering from surgery, following an illness or after childbirth. The focus is taken off the desire to get to the destination, and instead you learn to enjoy the journey.

Arrange the dates in advance so you both know when the sessions are scheduled and agree a time. It's a good idea for each person to alternate setting the time, venue, and creating a pleasurable ambience, to show their commitment to the process. Think about creating a peaceful environment (e.g. turning off your phone or TV). Wait until the children have gone to bed or are out of the house. Then create a warm, comfortable environment for the exercises (e.g. following a bath or shower, perhaps introducing candles and soft music). Consider using lotion or oil to massage each other, and you can be naked or wearing underwear or light clothing; whatever feels more comfortable.

The aim is for this to be a fun session and it is fine to vary it according to your own ideas. You may find a book or DVD about massage useful if you want to learn different techniques. Remember that the focus is enjoyment and pleasure. It doesn't always work immediately, and you may be unfamiliar with touching your partner in this way. Try not to worry about this. Acknowledge how the experience makes you feel and talk it through together afterwards. If you are seeing a therapist, you can take these thoughts back to your next session.

What to do

Take it in turns to give and receive touching. The aim of these exercises is for the toucher to focus on their feelings and the pleasure that they get from touching their partner. The idea is that, in order to stop feeling the pressure to perform, we must get fully in tune with what we are doing to our partner and focus on our own pleasure when doing this. If we are constantly focusing on our partner's pleasure, we can get preoccupied with whether we are getting it right and start to "spectator" ourselves as if watching someone else. I have slightly adapted the way I deliver the exercises and I encourage the toucher to try to focus on both their own pleasure and also that of their partner, in equal measure.

You might want to alternate on the same occasion, or to focus on one person in one session and the other person in the next. Take plenty of time to explore the other person's body, avoiding sexual areas: stroke, tickle, gently touch and massage them all over. Experiment with different sensations. Focus on your own pleasure in experiencing the texture, form, and temperature of the other person's body. Try to discover the degrees of pressure and types of touch that your partner finds most pleasurable by encouraging feedback or by placing your hand under their hand, so they can show you.

On your first turn at touching, get the other person to lie on their front, and massage their back, neck, arms, legs, hands, and feet (if they enjoy this).

On your second turn, get the other person to lie on their back and massage their neck, chest, stomach, shoulders, arms, and legs. You may also gently massage their scalp and face but avoid using lotion for these more sensitive areas.

When it is your turn to be touched, make sure you let the other person know what you like and don't like. Sometimes a touch will be too light, gentle or ticklish, or too heavy or uncomfortable. You can say how you feel, or move the other person's hand to where you want to be touched.

You might find it useful to talk about your experiences afterwards, e.g. "I really liked it when you…" or "I prefer this type of touch, I am not so keen on this..." Try not to be critical of your partner but sensitively let them know what you liked and what you would prefer instead, if you didn't like a particular touch or sensation.

If you try this approach and get stuck, then I would encourage you to take this experience into sex therapy. This information is a good starting point to help highlight what some of your issues might be. I use this approach with some couples to help us diagnose what might be going on for them.

Genital sensate focus

Ground rules

Having spent some time on non-genital sensate focus, you can bring in touching of the breasts and genital areas. You might want to spend several sessions or weeks on each phase of this stage before moving on to the next. At this point the ban on sexual intercourse is withdrawn, but some couples might like to agree a phased approach to reintroducing penetrative sexual intercourse until they are confident and comfortable with sexual foreplay.

When you start this phase of the programme, continue to pay attention to the other parts of the body that you explored in the previous sessions, as well as the new areas that you are incorporating. The main aim of these stages is to increase each person's pleasure and to create awareness of each other's responses to different types of stimulation. If one or both of you become aroused, this is fine, but it is not the aim of the exercise.

Again it may be useful to use massage oils or lotions. During genital stimulation, it is often useful to use an oil or water based lubricant (remember that oil-based products should not be used near condoms). There is more information in Appendix 3 about where to purchase genital lubricants.

Take care if you are using any oils, lotions or lubricants for the first time. Try them on a small patch of skin on your forearm to test if you have any adverse reactions before using them more liberally. This is particularly important around the genital areas where the skin can be more sensitive. Try different products if necessary. Make sure you won't be disturbed and create a relaxed environment and follow up the session by giving and receiving feedback. The focus is still on enjoyment.

What to do

Take it in turns to give and then receive touching, as before. You might want to incorporate a bit more of the body into each subsequent session, or to spend some time on each other in every session. It is worth spending at least five minutes each way. Position yourselves in a way that is comfortable for each person. First incorporate touching of breasts and nipples, then areas around the genitals, including the testicles. Then incorporate touching the genitals themselves (the clitoris and entrance to the vagina on a woman, or the penis, shaft, and glans on a man). After a while you may also want to incorporate oral as well as manual touching into both non-genital and genital touching. You may also want to experiment with vibrators. I discuss these in more detail later in this chapter.

When you have incorporated these stages for some time, you can incorporate the "teasing technique." Manually stimulate the other person's genitals gently at first, and then increase the speed of stimulation. Show each other how you like to be touched, take a rest, and then begin again. If orgasm occurs at this stage or later, that is fine, but it is not the aim of the process.

Finally, you may also want to incorporate some form of vaginal penetration, either using fingers or the man's penis. Make sure you apply adequate amounts of lubrication both to the woman's genital area and the man's penis. You may want to try first with one partner on top and then the other. Initially use minimal thrusting (this is particularly important if you have not engaged in sexual intercourse for some months or years). Later you can incorporate more thrusting.

A book by Weiner and Avery-Clark, *Sensate Focus in Sex Therapy: The Illustrated Manual*[2], also provides couples with more detailed information about undertaking the sensate focus programme, and contains helpful illustrations.

Separateness

When working with couples who struggle with low desire I will often talk about how each person maintains their "sense of self." What are they passionate about? What animates them outside of their relationship or family life? This could be a hobby, a social or political cause, an evening class they are taking, socialising with their friends, their work: any number of things. These are the kind of things that they would have talked about over dinner, when they were dating, and are still important. You are aiming for the thought about your partner: "Wow, there is so much about you I still don't know."

Sometimes I work with couples who are in a symbiotic relationship – each spouse has merged into the other. They do everything together. They do not like spending time apart and they rely on the other for companionship. This is not helpful. It can lead to couples becoming best friends but without any chemistry or sexual energy.

Esther Perel talks of the need to cross over a bridge to reach our spouses; the sense that we need distance in which we cross to meet our partner. Her research showed that when one partner saw the other outside of their usual context, it significantly increased feelings of sexual desire. For example, it might be you see your partner in animated conversation at a party, or giving a presentation at work. These sightings remind us of what attracted us in the first place. Creating an intimate team, the ability for deep connected communication whilst maintaining our separateness, can be a challenge but also provides the possibility of recreating a sense of discovery about the other person. This can be exciting and energising.

Playfulness

Establishing a balance of intimacy and separateness creates a space for flirtation and playfulness, which is another central theme in the concept of erotic intelligence. Playfulness is key to maintaining sexual desire and involves having a sense of humour, a willingness to experiment, and not taking things too seriously. Couples who are playful can be unselfconscious around sex.

In her book, Esther Perel talks about "cultivating play" with our partners. As children, playing comes naturally, and small children, as long as they feel safe, will seize the chance to play. I encourage couples to recreate that attitude to life, one of being uninhibited. For many, though, when facing sexual problems, being carefree is the last thing they can imagine. But the intimate team needs to understand how to play and what is unique about the way they play together. What is our specific style of play? Is it repetitive, and are both partners completely happy with that? If not, have we got into a bit of a rut, and how can we change? Often, it is down to attitude: we can learn new ways of trying and experiencing things, provided we are willing. There are various helpful tools that you can incorporate into your sexual repertoire. However, more important than this is Esther Perel's notion of needing to be playful rather than worrying about what body part we put where. We need to learn new ways of playing, and to bring an attitude of anticipation, playfulness and a lightness to the bedroom.

If we are stuck with limited tools, limited styles of playing and rigid ways of interacting, we are more likely to struggle with the notion of playfulness. If you told a child that every time they went into a playroom they had to get out exactly the same bricks, build them into exactly the same tower, and knock them down in exactly the same way, the child would rapidly lose his sense of adventure, his desire to explore and create, and his sense of playfulness. The question is not what you play but rather how playful you are.

What to do if we want to play in different ways

This again is where the intimate team comes in, to discuss issues openly. Suppose one of you wants to give and receive oral sex. What if your partner does not? Ultimately, you may have to give up on this, because all sexual activity *must* be consensual. My questions to a couple who had agreed not to try a particular sexual practice would be:

- Do you feel that in making this decision you drew together as an intimate team?

- Did you listen openly, and in a non-judgemental way, to your partner's requests and point of view?

74

🖉 Did you look at other options if you could not agree on what to do sexually together?

🖉 Did both parties come out of the discussion feeling respected, supported, listened to and valued?

If we are to develop erotic intelligence within marriage, we must engage in these kinds of discussions whilst remaining playful. This is a difficult tension to hold and one that you may need to revisit. We must remember, as we develop our sexual play, we are part of a team; this is not simply about our own needs or rules. We might need to set aside some of our preconceived ideas and be open to how our partner wants to engage in playing the game.

It is easy to be closed off to new experiences, thinking we know what we like and won't change. As a child I did not like having my feet touched. In adulthood the thought of a pedicure was very unappealing. But eventually I tried one, and now, ten years on, I love pedicures, particularly having my feet massaged. Sometimes we limit ourselves because we have such set rules about what we like. We can change – if we are willing to try new things.

Broadening your sexual repertoire – your sexual tool box

One of the best of the educational resources that I recommend to patients is the *Lovers' Guide* DVD range. These can be purchased through Amazon and other online stockists. The DVDs are endorsed by Relate, and are particularly appropriate for couples who want to expand their sexual repertoire. They include information about developing your relationship, building sensuality, arousing sex play, exploring oral sex, enhancing lovemaking, keeping intimacy alive, and overcoming problems. They do show couples (all married or in a relationship) demonstrating sexual techniques and making love. Unlike pornography, however, which is often focused on one person's own sexual gratification, the DVDs have a very relational focus which ensures that the couple are enhancing the experience for their partner as well as for themselves. There is also some very helpful educational commentary explaining what the couple is doing.

For those couples who may not feel comfortable watching this DVD, I also recommend the book *Sex: A Lover's Guide: The Ultimate Guide to Physical Attraction, Love-making Techniques and Sexual Relationships* by Judy Bastyra and Nitya Lacroix.[3] Again, the book is endorsed by Relate and covers a wide range of topics relating to sexual intimacy and broadening one's sexual repertoire.

The collections are regularly updated and I suggest you focus on those aimed at enhancing sex within a relationship.

Using a vibrator/experiencing an orgasm

Using a vibrator can be the most effective way of extending your sexual repertoire and increasing sexual pleasure. Men and women vary in their experience of sexual desire: men are more likely to feel it spontaneously; women need to be aroused and can feel under huge pressure to be so. And of course, the pressure stops them feeling aroused. This can be difficult for the husband, who may be trying all kinds of different things to arouse his partner, and the unspoken pressure of this compounds the problem.

This is the female version of performance anxiety. For women, vibrators can help to reduce this, because they enable many women to become aroused much quicker than when using manual stimulation. They can also immediately take the pressure off the male partner to stimulate his wife. The woman can feel empowered because she can position the vibrator to best enjoy the sensation without the need to direct her partner, which sometimes feels disheartening to both parties and can actually be a turn-off. Many men say it can also be a very arousing experience for the man to see his wife become aroused using a vibrator, and thus is a positive experience for him as well.

Vibrators are regularly recommended by psychosexual therapists as part of self-growth and couple programmes. You may not be comfortable with the thought of using a sex aid, but just as some people need glasses to enhance their sight, many women find using a vibrator significantly enhances arousal, which increases sexual desire and leads to them having orgasms. Most men expect to achieve orgasm as the end of sexual arousal, but women don't have to do so in order to feel sexual satisfaction, although many do want to do so. There is also a misconception that women regularly experience orgasm through vaginal penetration: probably only about 25 percent of women experience orgasm this way. Orgasm through clitoral stimulation is much more common. A vibrator can be used for both clitoral and vaginal stimulation and there are many different models that cater for this. Whether or not orgasms matter to you can be discussed as part of your intimate team conversations. I have included information in Appendix 3 about where you can buy a vibrator.

Play creatively

What do you think sex should include? Does it have to involve penetration? Do both partners have to orgasm? Varying what you do as a couple can be more interesting. It can just involve varying sexual positions, but it can also include oral sex, or mutual stimulation of your own or your partner's genitals. Thinking of sex in this way can be liberating. It also can free couples up, allowing one spouse to give the "gift" of sexual pleasure to the other without the need for this to always be reciprocated.

I sometimes see couples who present with sexual problems where one or both partners regularly masturbate on their own. This is often because the couple's sexual experience is not enjoyable and perhaps there are sexual difficulties. The habit of secretive masturbation can be destructive and does not nurture an intimate team, especially if this is never addressed by the couple. It may be that the wife has found penetrative sex too painful, so the husband relies on masturbation alone; or the husband keeps losing his erections, so the wife achieves orgasm alone. In both cases, the issues are not discussed and there is no attempt to solve the problems.

Working as an intimate team, though, both couples would be able to draw together to talk about what is happening and to consider how they will seek help. Visiting their GP would be a good place to start, but each couple could still enjoy sex, even if it is non-penetrative. This creates a completely different feel and enables the couple to pull together in order to enjoy either receiving from or giving pleasure to their partner. They can cuddle afterwards, feel emotionally close, and resolve to tackle the difficulties as a unit.

What if one of you is too tired at the end of the day for full sex? Perhaps the wife uses her vibrator while her husband caresses her breasts. Or the wife gives the husband oral sex or stimulates his penis with her hand. Many couples have never thought about giving sexual pleasure as a gift to their partner. If one spouse is too exhausted to participate, then the couple may negotiate for the aroused partner to stimulate themselves, with their partner lying next to them in close physical contact. This might not be ideal, and I wouldn't advocate this as a regular practice, but it is a way for both spouses to get their needs met. One partner enjoys a sexual release and the other can be non-sexual. This can revolutionise the way they think about sexual contact because it gives both the option for sexual pleasure, in the presence of their partner, but without the need for this to always be reciprocal and without the pressure to perform. In this way, the sexual experience is shared, rather than secrecy seeping in, which undermines the intimate team and can be very destructive long term.

Good Enough Sex (GES)

Finally I am going to mention "Good Enough Sex" – a concept developed by sex experts Metz and McCarthy. They say:

78

No one has a perfect sex life. Hype sets you up for self-defeating performance demands and disappointment. Get real! Instead think: really good sex, enduring desire, realistically satisfying, high quality, and genuine couple sex – sex that provides a supportive energy and that most days gives support to your daily life.[4]

So, what does the Good Enough Sex model mean? It means relinquishing our set ideas, fuelled by the media, that sex should be a certain way. In fact, many things will influence our sexual functioning and we need to have an open mind. Sometimes sexual intimacy will be passionate and exciting, other times good, and sometimes just okay.

When I talked about the timetabling model earlier in the chapter, I suggested that, very much like doing exercise, we need to prioritise time to be intimate. And in the same way, some exercise can be energising and feel great, and other times it will be just okay, but we are glad that we did it. Exercise is energising and life-affirming, and so is sex.

It is good for the soul to desire and be desired; the Good Enough Sex model reminds us that this is possible even if the sexual experience is not perfect. This may be because of a sexual problem, such as erectile dysfunction or painful sex, but by talking openly and without judgement, a couple can be brought closer together. Maybe a spouse will be really truthful about how sad they feel that sex is difficult, and they have begun to internalise the failure and feel it's a reflection on them. These painful conversations can be very powerful in strengthening the couple's bond and deepening intimacy.

References

1. Esther Perel, *Mating in Captivity: Sex, Lies and Domestic Bliss*, (London: Hodder & Stoughton, 2007).

2. L. Weiner and C. Avery-Clark, *Sensate Focus in Sex Therapy: The Illustrated Manual*, (New York: Routledge, 2017).

3. Judy Bastyra and Nitya Lacroix, *Sex: A Lover's Guide – The Ultimate Guide to Physical Attraction, Love-making Techniques and Sexual Relationships*, (London: Southwater, 2015).

4. Michael E. Metz and Barry W. McCarthy, *Enduring Desire: Your Guide to Lifelong Intimacy*, (London: Routledge, 2010).

CHAPTER FOUR

Forsaking All Others:
The Damaging Impact
of Pornography

T he subject of pornography is a huge one and I am only going to give you an overview of some particularly relevant points. Pornography has become an accepted part of our culture and is having a massive impact on the way teenagers and young people see sex, as well as adults.

Research commissioned by the National Society for the Prevention of Cruelty to Children (NSPCC) and the Children's Commissioner for England said many teenagers were at risk of becoming desensitised by pornography.[1] The study showed that about 53 percent of eleven to sixteen year olds have seen explicit material online, usually (94 percent) by the age of fourteen. A recent article on the BBC website looked at the increasing numbers of men accessing sex therapy through NHS clinics for erection problems, attributed to an addiction to internet pornography.[2] These men have become desensitised to arousal with their partners, affecting their ability to get and maintain an erection. Among my patients, I have noticed a significant increase in the number of men in their twenties and thirties who feel that watching pornography has become detrimental to their sexual functioning. They have often decided to reduce their viewing and recognise the effect of accessing much more explicit hard-core pornography. They realise that the bar to becoming aroused is increasingly being made higher by what they are viewing; rather like a drug addict looking for a more intense high.

Gary Wilson, a freelance consultant and author, has written an interesting book titled *Your Brain on Porn – Internet Pornography and the Emerging Science of Addiction*.[3] He proposes that a growing body of research in neuroscience is confirming what many individuals have discovered for themselves – internet pornography can be very addictive and ultimately damaging.

When having sex or watching pornography, dopamine – a neurotransmitter – is released into a region of the brain responsible for emotion and learning, and gives the viewer a sense of craving. It also creates a sense of heightened pleasure, by activating the rewards circuitry in our brains that make us feel good, and plays an important role in memory. This is the same dopamine response that drug addicts experience. The next time the viewer gets the urge for more sexual pleasure, small surges of dopamine are released in the brain, reminding the user how good it was when they got their fix last time.

Norepinephrine is another neurotransmitter, often associated with stress and the fight or flight response which makes us alert. It is the brain's version of adrenaline, and whether we are remembering a wonderful sexual experience we had with our partner or an arousing sexual image onscreen, the information is easily recalled with the help of norepinephrine.

Sex and pornography also trigger the release of oxytocin and vasopressin. Oxytocin is sometimes referred to as the "bonding" hormone. Oxytocin levels rise when couples have close physical contact, and it is released during orgasm. This is usually seen as a positive part of sexual intimacy, but for users of pornography it can have a negative impact, because the viewer's brain bonds to the source of release – in this case, the pornography. This bonding is especially prevalent when the activity is reinforced through repetition.

The body also releases endorphins, natural opiates that create a high, a wave of pleasure over the whole body. After sexual release serotonin levels also change, bringing a sense of calm well-being and relaxation. These hormones help to lay down the long-term memories for the cells and reinforce the behaviour. This is positive when it reinforces pleasure with a partner but can be damaging when it reinforces pleasure associated with viewing pornography. This is particularly challenging when a person wants to reduce or stop watching pornography, because the brain circuitry has been reinforced to repeat the addiction-forming behaviour. After repeated viewing, many users of pornography also find they need more intense imagery to activate a sense of sexual arousal. Over time, the brain starts to moderate the dopamine that is released, by reducing the dopamine receptors needed for viewing pornography. In response to these, viewers will look for new and novel stimulation to get the increased levels of dopamine, which then gives them the same high.

Gary Wilson references studies that looked at scans of the brain in internet addicts, both gaming addicts and pornography addicts. They show the presence of the same core brain changes as are found in substance addicts. Wilson explains that addiction is the most extensively studied mental disorder. The studies have identified the link in behavioural and substance additions:

… the same molecular switch initiates key addiction-related brain changes (and thus behaviours) in both chemical and behavioural addictions. These kind of discoveries are the reason that addiction experts have no doubt that both behavioural and substance addictions are fundamentally one disorder.[3]

The studies confirm that in both groups the altered brain chemistry that occurs in these addictive behaviours actually changes the structure of the brain and the way it functions. This is particularly alarming because research also reveals that addictive pornography has the ability to significantly affect a man's ability to get and maintain an erection, reach orgasm, and ejaculate.

Pornography is not relational. It does not require anything back from the consumer. It allows the viewer to absorb its content without any requirement to read their partner, to respond to another's touch or gaze. It becomes much easier to understand how difficult it can be for couples to engage in satisfying relationship-enhancing sexual intimacy, if one or both spouses are hooked on pornography. One or both partners may find they experience a reduced sense of arousal with their partner. For some couples, this is so marked, it actually impacts significantly on their ability to even get aroused at all with their partner.

The Bible makes no specific reference to pornography as we know it, because it did not exist in the same way it does today. The Bible does however give us clear instructions about not coveting, which means to "yearn to possess":

You shall not covet your neighbour's house. You shall not covet your neighbour's wife, or his male or female servant, his ox or donkey, or anything that belongs to your neighbour.

Exodus 20:17

I do not want to incite any sort of shame. You may be a Christian who uses pornography and you feel completely comfortable with that. But from my clinical experience and discussing the topic within my own Christian community, many Christians do not feel comfortable watching pornography but do it anyway. We are reminded that we are all created in God's image, both the viewer and the participant in pornography. Those involved in sex work find it is far from glamorous, sexually gratifying or affirming. It is usually demoralising, physically gruelling, and demeaning to the human spirit. Many sex workers, including those involved in pornography, do not do so through choice. Some are there because of coercion and fear. Others have a very distorted sense of themselves, often resulting from inadequate early attachments in life and subsequently a disrupted childhood. Lack of core self-worth then impacts their life choices (such as working in the sex industry) and this further perpetuates low self-worth. We all have things in our lives that we struggle with, and for many Christians pornography is one of them. For others the challenges will be different. Shame can overwhelm us so that we feel separated from God and our church community – the last thing that God would want.

God places parameters around sex for our own well-being and because He loves us. These parameters are often not observed in secular society. With pornography, my focus is not moral or religious, but rather cautionary: I have seen first-hand the damage that pornography can do, and this is the most powerful argument for abstaining. God wants us to enjoy sexual freedom with our partners. Pornography can alter the way our brain works, affect sexual arousal with our spouse, and erode the intimacy that we share.

It can be very lonely, if you or your partner is struggling with an addiction to pornography, especially if you cannot share this with anyone else. In an intimate team, maybe you can discuss this with your partner and consider where you can find help. If you don't feel you are in an intimate team, and cannot talk to your partner, then find a close Christian friend who won't judge you but will support you as you seek help. I have included some information in Appendix 5 about organisations which offer support to sex addicts and their partners, including addiction to pornography, and details of an online support, *Covenant Eyes*, which offers software to help people who want to stop using pornography.

If you are interested in understanding the altered brain chemistry that is associated with pornography addiction, Gary Wilson has an excellent website, including access to his TED talks, at: www.yourbrainonporn.com

Whatever we struggle with in our lives, be it pornography or another stumbling block, we can take comfort in these words:

For I am convinced that neither death nor life, neither angels nor demons, neither the present nor the future, nor any powers, neither height nor depth, nor anything else in all creation, will be able to separate us from the love of God that is in Christ Jesus our Lord.

Romans 8:38–39

References

1. E. Martellozzo, A. Monaghan, J.R. Adler, et al., *A quantitative and qualitative examination of the impact of online pornography on the values, attitudes, beliefs, and behaviours of children and young people*, (London: Middlesex University, 2017).

2. www.bbc.co.uk/newsbeat/article/37058019/easy-access-to-online-porn-is-damaging-mens-health-says-nhs-therapist

3. Gary Wilson, *Your Brain on Porn – Internet Pornography and the Emerging Science of Addiction*, (Margate: Commonwealth Publishing, 2014).

Recommended reading

Paula Hall, *Understanding and Treating Sex Addiction*, (London: Routledge, 2012).

Paula Hall, *Sex Addiction: The Partner's Perspective*, London: Routledge, 2015).

CHAPTER FIVE

From This Day Forward: Seeking Help and What to Expect

The gift of marriage brings husband and wife together
in the delight and tenderness of sexual union
and joyful commitment to the end of their lives.

Church of England marriage service

If you are having sexual problems in your marriage, there are various sources of help available, and this chapter will consider what is out there and what you can expect. You may believe the problem is entirely psychological/emotional (in the mind), or that it is entirely physical (in the body) – but I would strongly advise, whatever your own thoughts, that you consider seeing your GP first so that you can rule out any easily treated underlying physical cause. It is frustrating for couples if they have invested time and money in seeking help with a sex therapist for something like dyspareunia (painful sex), only to discover a year down the line that the woman is experiencing recurrent thrush, and once this is treated with medication, the pain subsides. The same applies to something like erectile dysfunction. Talking therapies can help the couple find effective ways to communicate and to strengthen the intimate team, but there are some conditions that I discuss in the following chapters that would benefit from more medical intervention, certainly to begin with. Some couples benefit from a dual approach so they address the medical issue at the same time as having therapy, and this can be very effective too.

For some people, past sexual problems, relationship difficulties or many other factors mean that, despite the fact they are married, their marriages are effectively sexless. Statistics are hard to find but anecdotal evidence suggests that sexless marriage is on the increase. But does it matter if we do not have sex any more?

I believe it does matter. Historically, Christians and the church in general shared a reputation for being anti-sex, but today's marriage preparation and marriage courses focus on the importance of sexual intimacy. When we take our wedding vows, we recognise the importance of joining together with our spouse in a physical union and the part this plays in deepening our commitment to each other.

With my body I honour you, all that I am I give to you, and all that I have I share with you, within the love of God, Father, Son and Holy Spirit.

Church of England marriage vows

We might think of this vow as only about sharing our material wealth, but I have always thought of this as literally "all that I have", which includes our bodies. However, some couples rarely have sex and are quite happy with this. If they do not perceive this to be a problem, and they consider themselves a strong intimate team, then nor would I consider it to be a problem. However, I all too often meet individuals who are seeking help because their partner has unilaterally decided they no longer wish to be sexually intimate, with no discussion, and it can be terribly painful for the partner who does not want to live this way. For other couples, though, sexual intimacy may occur more regularly, say once a month, but it is strained; one partner feels pressured into having sex and neither feels particularly emotionally close afterwards. This couple would not theoretically be defined as having a sexless marriage, but clearly, they are not happy with the situation and I would question what was happening in their marriage more generally as to why this had not been addressed. Perhaps there is a functional problem – erectile dysfunction or painful sex. Or there may be wider tension in the marriage and the lack of intimacy is just a symptom of this. Perhaps the couple have never functioned as an intimate team and it would feel very alien to them to talk about their needs and desires in this area.

It may be that you have simply fallen out of the habit of having sex; if this is you, then the first three chapters of this book may have been helpful.

Seeing your GP

I strongly recommend going to see your GP before you do anything else. If the sexual issue can be pinpointed to difficulty with a body part, i.e. the penis or vagina, then it is very important that the GP undertakes a physical examination to ensure there is no obvious physical abnormality. I have seen a number of men who have presented with erection problems and I have been the first person from whom they have sought help. I do not undertake physical examinations myself in clinic, which is the norm with most sex therapists. As I have been completing the assessment it became clear that the men were experiencing pain when they had an erection, which we discovered was related to a tight foreskin. I was able to refer the patients to an urologist to discuss surgery and other options to resolve this. Ultimately, we could have done all the talking therapy in the world about the erections and the marriage but we wouldn't have been able to address the underlying problem of pain.

Women

If you are a woman seeing your GP about dyspareunia (painful sex), or vaginismus (an inability to tolerate vaginal penetration), your doctor is likely to ask you questions about your pain or discomfort, your lifestyle, and any other relevant medical and emotional issues. They will need to examine you, to see if you have any obvious physical cause for the pain. This is likely to include examination of your external genitals or vulva, which includes the opening of the vagina (introitus), the lips (labia majora/minor) surrounding this, and the clitoris. They may apply pressure, sometimes using a cotton bud, in certain areas to see where you feel the pain. You may also need an internal examination which your doctor would do with gloved fingers and possibly a speculum (a plastic instrument which is inserted into the vagina and gently widened to allow better visual examination).

Your doctor may want to do a swab and a urine test to check for infection, and possibly blood tests to check your hormone profile and general health. If your GP is not confident in diagnosing or treating you, or they think you require more specific tests, they may refer you to a gynaecologist or another hospital specialist.

Men

If you are a man then your GP will want to examine your penis, including the shaft and the glans and the scrotal area and testes. If you have a foreskin they will want to ensure that the foreskin is easily retractable. If you have symptoms of an enlarged prostate gland, such as a weak urine stream and/or urgent or frequent urination, your doctor may also want to examine your prostate. This is done by inserting a gloved finger into your rectum to feel the size and shape of the prostate gland. Even if you do not have symptoms of an enlarged prostate, your GP may still want to check your prostate anyway as a form of health screening for prostate cancer, which will be done in combination with a blood test.

Your GP probably will not have time to take an extensive history in the way a sex therapist can, so they will focus on a physical examination and they may also want to organise for you to have some bloods taken. This will give the GP useful information about your general health. These typically include thyroid and liver function, a full blood count, which can help to identify if you are anaemic, and a blood glucose test to screen for diabetes. They may also want to check your cholesterol levels. All these are important markers, especially for erectile dysfunction. We know that erectile dysfunction can indicate underlying vascular disease which I talk more about in the next chapter. The GP may also want to check your hormone profile, which will include testosterone, especially if you are experiencing low libido (sexual desire).

If you are over the age of fifty, the GP may want to check a marker in your blood that can help diagnosis prostate cancer and this is usually done in combination with the physical check of the prostate.

As well as checking your bloods the GP may also want to take your blood pressure to ensure that it is within normal range. Prolonged hypertension (high blood pressure) can be a sign of someone suffering with stress. Some of the blood tests such as the hormone profile and blood pressure measurement may need to be rechecked, as it is not usual for hormone problems or hypertension to be diagnosed with a one-off reading.

When the problem isn't physical...

What if your GP does not diagnose a physical problem? There may be a whole host of other reasons why sex is difficult for you. This could be linked to past sexual experiences, or lack of adequate information about foreplay and sexual intercourse. It could be that you are experiencing relationship difficulties with your spouse, which are impacting how your body responds when you are touched. Sexual difficulties can be very varied and complex because no two people are the same. Seeking professional help can enable you to look at all these issues and provide you with a renewed sense of hope.

Finding a therapist

This can be a daunting decision, but also an exciting one. Sex therapy is a talking therapy, where individuals or couples work with a qualified therapist to explore ways to manage their sexual and/or relationship problems. Sex therapists can have different professional backgrounds but they all have more time than the average GP. A GP's consultation times are usually very limited, perhaps just ten minutes. This can be challenging because the causes of sexual difficulties can be both many and complex, as we have seen. Consultation times with a sex therapist, however, will usually be around fifty minutes in duration. You may be able to see a sex therapist on the NHS, although sadly these services are limited. Discuss it with your GP, who can refer you if this service is available in your local area. Alternatively, there are lots of therapists who practise privately.

The quality of the relationship you have with your therapist will be crucial in deciding whether you and your sex life benefit from the sessions. Allow two or three sessions to get to know each other, and to start to trust; but if, after four sessions, you are still feeling uncomfortable, then discuss this with the therapist. Make sure they are clear on what kind of help you need, and if things do not improve, consider finding an alternative therapist. It can take individuals or couples two or three attempts before they find the right person.

Always check that your therapist belongs to a recognised professional organisation, with a proper code of conduct and a complaints procedure. All practising therapists should have clinical supervision, someone they talk to about their caseload; this is mandatory practice. This process is confidential, so the therapist will not reveal your identity during any discussions about your case.

Some therapists will ask you to read and sign their terms of working, which will often cover issues such as confidentiality, payment, and their cancellation policy. Don't be afraid to confront your therapist if you are not happy. If you are looking specifically for a sex and relationship therapist then I would direct you towards two charities: COSRT (the College of Sex and Relationship Therapists) and Relate (see Appendix 5).

Some sex therapists (this is extremely rare) touch clients intimately as part of the therapy they offer, and vice versa, with the end goal often being full sexual intercourse between client and therapist. I have never met or worked with therapists who practise in this way but I have read articles about a couple of therapists who believe that touching their clients is a helpful part of the therapeutic work. It is worth checking at the start that any therapist you see does not do this. As well as finding a therapist, if you have a few close friends who are happy to pray for you as a couple while you are having therapy, such additional support can be helpful. Pray for God's peace as you embark on this journey. It may feel like a big step but it can be very fruitful. I hope this will prove to be a new and exciting possibility for you, for renewed couple intimacy and an enriched relationship.

A final note

If you feel that you and your spouse are unable to talk about infidelity or any of the other sensitive issues in this book, then you might need to seek professional help. If your spouse is unwilling to communicate or enter into couple counselling, then you might need to seek individual therapy to help you decide how to move forward. As Christians, when we take our wedding vows in front of our spouse, family, and friends, we are making a solemn promise to do what we can to uphold these for the rest of our lives together.

Sometimes, despite our best efforts, marriages break down, for many different reasons. If, as you read this, you feel your marriage is beyond repair, then I would still urge you to seek professional help, and see if that can make a difference and the marriage can continue. However, if you are in a relationship that is unsafe, perhaps because your partner is violent, then remember that God does not expect you to honour your marriage vows at the risk of your life. If you are facing a situation like this then I would really encourage you to seek the support you need, so that you can think about the options available. We all have choices, even if these are hard choices. (Support Organisations can be found in Appendix 5.)

Regardless of the reasons for doing so, if you do separate eventually, at least you will know you did as much as you could to honour the promises you made to try to work through the good times and the bad. If separation is inevitable, you as a couple can choose to do this respectfully and fairly, which is particularly important if you have children. A couples therapist will be able to help you navigate the difficult path ahead.

'For I know the plans I have for you,' declares the LORD, 'plans to prosper you and not to harm you, plans to give you hope and a future. Then you will call on me and come and pray to me, and I will listen to you.'

Jeremiah 29:11–12

PART TWO

In Sickness and in Health: Managing Sexual Difficulties

*Let us not become weary in doing good, for at the proper time
we will reap a harvest if we do not give up.*

Galatians 6:9

Introduction to
Sexual Difficulties

In this section of the book, I cover a different sexual difficulty in each chapter. Some chapters are clearly aimed at either men or women, but the chapters on sexual desire and sexual pain are aimed at both men and women. You may start by looking at a chapter on a particular difficulty, one you need help with, but I suggest reading all the chapters, regardless of whether you have that particular problem. None of us know what we will meet later in life, and sex has its seasons. We will be better placed to address difficulties if we already understand something about them, before we experience them.

Many of us will be familiar with the expression "terrible twos." It's a term used to describe the very normal tantrums that toddlers often have, around the age of two, as they appreciate their separateness from their parents and want to assert their independence. Many a parent will be alarmed when they momentarily wonder what is happening to their usually angelic child, only to remember: "This is what everyone talks about!" It is the same with sexual difficulties. It is often the not knowing that is the frightening bit – problems can lose much of their power and fear if we are able to name them and recognise such difficulties are very common and treatable.

In the Introduction I explained that my aim when discussing sexual difficulties is to arm you with the tools you need to "triage" yourself. This means that I will not necessarily provide you with every detail or treatment option for all the sexual problems, but rather give you enough information to understand the problem for yourself. You may not, at the moment, know if what you are experiencing even has a name or a diagnosis. I will walk you through the steps that I would assess if we met in person, to help you understand some of the potential causes and the available treatment options.

Once a couple I am working with understands what the problem is, how it might have developed, and what they can do to treat it, they feel more empowered. This is a crucial part of resolving any sexual problem. You do not have to live with the problem and there are lots of choices to help resolve these difficulties, as the following chapters will show.

I often think that being a sex therapist is a little bit like being a detective. I work with the individual or couple to piece together all the relevant bits of information, and at the end of the assessment, we can see the overall picture, enabling us to determine the best course of action.

Any sex therapist will take an in-depth history from a new client, and this will include questions that will reveal what factors have contributed to the problem, how long they have been occurring, and so on. There are three key factors: predisposing, precipitating, and maintaining factors.

Predisposing factors

These are things that might have made you more likely to find sexual intimacy or related aspects more problematic. For instance:

- How did you learn about sex? Was it positive or was it talked about in a shameful or negative way? If so, this may have set up a negative outlook on sex.

- Have you experienced any sort of sexual trauma or sexual abuse? If so, this may have impacted your view of sexual intimacy. Have you been able to talk to your spouse about this? Have you had any counselling or therapy?

- What were the unspoken messages you received from your parents or main carers about sex as you grew up? Did they sleep in separate rooms? Were they physically affectionate with each other?

- Did you have other sexual relationships before you met your spouse? If so, what were these like? If these were not positive experiences, this may impact how you view sex with your spouse.

- Have you ever experienced any sort of sexual problems in the past such as erectile dysfunction, vaginismus or dyspareunia? If so, could the fear of this returning be having an impact on your desire to initiate or engage in sex with your new partner?

- Did you grow up in a culture where sex was only about procreation? In this case you may find it difficult to view sex as an expression of love, a release, an act of self-soothing, and for physical pleasure.

Precipitating (triggering) factors

These things may have been a trigger just prior to experiencing the sexual problem and sometimes we can make a direct link. So, for example, with erectile dysfunction, if a man has just started on a medication, this could trigger sexual difficulties as a side effect. Women can find sex painful following the trigger of childbirth.

Maintaining factors

In many ways I consider maintaining factors to be the most important to consider. Many couples will experience blips in their sexual relationship, but why is it that some couples are able to manage these themselves, or seek help and move on, and yet other couples get stuck? These are often related to their ability to draw together as an intimate team and manage the difficulties in a constructive way. Sometimes the maintaining factors are specifically related to the predisposing factors. So, for example, if one person has grown up in a family with parents who never talked about sex, then when they find themselves or their partner struggling, they do not have the language or the confidence to tackle it. The problem is never discussed and is left untreated.

In each chapter I will focus on particular precipitating factors that we know can be pertinent to a given problem. For example, we know that chronic vaginal thrush can be a trigger for sexual pain in some women. Some medications can trigger erectile difficulties. The precipitating or triggering factors will vary from chapter to chapter, but on the whole, the predisposing and maintaining factors share a commonality that doesn't vary much. I won't therefore repeat these in every chapter, but will list if there is an exception to this.

Situational or absolute?

Next, we need to discover if the problem is situational or absolute. Is it there all the time (absolute) or does it only occur in specific situations (situational)? An example might be when a man can get an erection when he stimulates himself, but not when making love with his wife. This gives the therapist a clue that there is likely to be an underlying psychological or emotional cause. It could be anxiety, for example, or there might be specific difficulties within the relationship.

If the problem is absolute, i.e. it happens all the time and does not change in different situations, this can suggest to the therapist that there may be an underlying physical cause. These questions should always be held lightly by the therapist in the context of a wider assessment because situations are not always black and white. The information gathered when we ask these questions, however, can be very helpful in enabling the therapist and the patient or couple to reach a shared understanding of what the difficulties are and how they might best tackle these.

Diagnosis

Sexual difficulties are classified according to the American Psychiatric Association's *Diagnostic and Statistical Manual of Mental Disorders, Fifth Edition* (DSM5).[1] This is a medical classification that outlines the criteria required to be able to diagnosis a problem and then consider the treatment options available. It is a useful tool for clinicians because it means that diagnosis and care can be fairly easily standardised, and tends to be less subjective. If you are interested in reading more specific details about any sexual dysfunction you can buy a copy of the manual.

I am going to outline to the reader the specific kind of information that a clinician would be looking for, in order to formulate a medical diagnosis, and this is done with the DSM5 loosely in mind. I think it is useful for the reader to understand the medical framework that specialists will use to diagnose and treat a specific problem. If we understand the sexual problem as fully as we can, then it helps the patient or couple to feel empowered. It moves them from a passive receiver position, with an all-knowing "specialist", to being an informed participant who can fully engage in making the best choices for them.

Seeking help

In Chapter 5 I have outlined where and how to seek help and I encourage everyone, whether they believe the problem to be physical or psychological, to see their GP first of all, before going to see a sex therapist. Sex therapy is never a waste of time, because it enables couples to understand how to create an intimate team and hone their communication skills, as well as managing sexual difficulties, but it is important to seek treatment in the right order.

In the following chapters I will give readers an overview of the treatment options available, whether this is with a medical focus through the GP or hospital specialist, or with a sex therapist. The treatment options will not be exhaustive because treatments are constantly evolving, and no two practitioners work in exactly the same way, but it will give readers a sense of what to expect.

Contraception

Hormone-based contraception – the contraceptive pill, the coil, the implant, and the contraceptive injection – can significantly affect a woman's sexual desire and it is important to know this. If a woman is starting on a hormonal contraceptive, then it is important that she gives it three to six months to settle down, before making a decision about whether she wants to continue or whether it is having a detrimental effect on her libido. After all, it rather defeats the object of using contraception, if all desire for sex diminishes or goes completely!

Some couples decide to use a barrier method such as the diaphragm or condoms. These are a good non-hormonal alternative, but they can interrupt love-making. This can be particularly challenging if the couple are trying to manage a sexual difficulty such as erectile dysfunction or sexual pain. The stop-start nature of introducing them can put some couples off, so it is worth thinking about this when working out what will be best for you.

Pregnancy

There are a number of issues to think about around sex and pregnancy. The first is that many couples feel sex changes when they start trying for a baby. They may decide they want to conceive and start off with a fairly relaxed approach, but it doesn't take many months for them to feel disappointed when they do not get pregnant. The act of sex, one that felt purely about pleasure and closeness, now has another focus which can make it feel functional. Perhaps couples are suddenly making love much more frequently than they were. The NHS guidelines for conception recommend that a couple make love every two to three days. This can start off as a novelty but as the months go on, this wears off and sex can feel very pressured. There is no easy answer to this, but being an intimate team is important here. It is crucial that you talk to your spouse about how to keep the enjoyment alive and it may help to read Chapter 3 on broadening your sexual repertoire. Something like introducing a vibrator can be helpful to increase arousal.

I also think it is important that couples continue to make love during the times of the month that are less fertile, so some of the focus remains on their pleasure and intimacy, and not purely on getting pregnant. The NHS provides some useful information for those trying to conceive: www.nhs.uk/conditions/pregnancy-and-baby/getting-pregnant/

And with a baby on the way?

It is wonderful when a couple discover they are pregnant, but this can sometimes pose other challenges. Should we stop having sex? Will sex harm the baby? Typically, it is safe to have sex throughout pregnancy, but it is important to discuss this with your midwife. Every situation is different and there may be other medical issues that need to be taken into consideration.

During pregnancy, a woman's body changes significantly. Perhaps she loves this; perhaps she does not. Some men embrace their wife's changing body shape; others do not. How a couple feels during pregnancy can vary hugely. This is another example of how important it is for a couple to be able to talk candidly about how they are feeling. Issues such as how a partner feels about his wife's pregnant body need to be handled with great sensitivity, but it is possible for couples to share these feelings respectfully, and for the truth to be said in a way that draws both together.

During pregnancy, hormones can significantly impact how sexual a woman feels. Some women notice a significant increase in their libido, particularly in the second trimester (from 13 to 27 weeks). This can be lovely for the couple or it can be challenging, especially if the man does not find his pregnant wife's changing body very arousing. Ultimately, we feel how we feel and it is important to be kind to one another and to try to explore how to get the best out of a situation that may not be perfect.

When the baby arrives

The delivery of the baby can also impact how the couple feel about sex. Most women, even if they have had an uncomplicated delivery, will feel sore afterwards, for some weeks or even months. If a woman has had a caesarean or episiotomy (surgical cut to enlarge the entrance to the vagina), both can be very painful, and recovery may take longer. If the childbirth has been traumatic, then both partners may be affected by this and not be able to imagine engaging in sexual intimacy quickly.

Having a child is an extraordinary and wonderful thing, and it also changes the dynamic in the family. There were two, now there are three, or four or more. Both parents are likely to feel tired with broken sleep and a new sense of responsibility about how to care for this little baby. It is so important that they talk about what they want for their relationship before the baby arrives. Organising time together as a couple can become more challenging and you need to have a plan for how you are going to create this couple time, because otherwise it will not happen. This adjustment and the loss of spontaneity can be difficult.

Breastfeeding can also impact the couple sexually. The breasts will have a new function, and no longer be primarily a part of the body that brings pleasure. A woman may find that her breasts are particularly sensitive or sore, and she does not want her partner to touch them in a sexual way. Breastfeeding can also impact a woman's libido. The change in hormones can result in less vaginal lubrication, which can make arousal more difficult and sex more painful. Using liberal amounts of vaginal lubrication can be really helpful as well as ensuring the woman is adequately aroused before penetrative sex is attempted.

If you have had a baby and you are struggling to rekindle the sexual intimacy in your marriage, or you feel this has changed, then you might want to read the chapters on communication and broadening your sexual repertoire. This can be particularly helpful if penetrative sexual intercourse is going to be difficult for a while following childbirth, but you are still keen to have sexual intimacy in other ways. If you are experiencing a sexual problem, then you can read the specific chapter that is relevant. In my experience, the most common issues after childbirth are dyspareunia and decreased sexual desire.

As a general rule, sex therapy should not be offered to a couple where the woman is pregnant. The period is so relatively short, with so many transient variable factors, that it is not a good time to embark on therapy. I would also encourage any couple to wait for six months following the birth of a baby before starting therapy. You need to give yourselves some time for life to settle down and regain some routine before you set aside more time to focus back on your marriage and overcoming any difficulties.

If you are struggling to get pregnant and the strain of this is causing relational tension or the introduction of a baby is having a negative impact on your relationship, then therapy can be helpful.

The menopause

The word menopause means your last menstrual period. "Meno" refers to your menstrual cycle and "pause" means to stop. The medical definition of being menopausal is that you have not had a period for one year. The menopause occurs when your ovaries stop producing eggs and, as a result, the levels of some hormones fall – specifically, oestrogen, progesterone, and testosterone. The term perimenopause is often used to describe a woman who is experiencing menopausal symptoms but still having periods. These periods are often more irregular than they used to be.

The hormones oestrogen and progesterone work together to regulate your menstrual cycle and the production of eggs. During the perimenopause, the levels of these hormones fluctuate a lot, and it is often the imbalance of these hormones which leads to menopausal symptoms occurring. These can significantly affect a woman's sexual relationship. For some women, these symptoms only occur for a few months and then their periods stop completely. However, other women experience symptoms for many months or even many years, before their periods stop.

The menopause is a normal process that every woman will go through, but its symptoms can significantly affect a woman's life. These changes can also impact the partner and wider family unit. The adjustment to the hormone fluctuation can affect many aspects of a woman's life, including her self-esteem, emotional and physical well-being, and sexual functioning. Body fat distribution can change a woman's body shape, which can also make a difference to how the woman feels about herself. We know hormones significantly influence our emotional and thought processes. Physical changes will also occur that can quite significantly affect a woman's sexual desire and enjoyment of sexual intimacy, especially if sex becomes painful, as it often does.

I have touched upon many of these factors in the following chapters that look at female sexual problems. The menopause is a very big subject and could warrant a book in itself, so if you would like more information on the menopause, and how to manage symptoms, you can find this on the websites listed below. Dr Louise Newton is a specialist GP who runs a menopause clinic and she has created a good website: www.menopausedoctor.co.uk

The NHS also provides useful information. If you are experiencing menopausal symptoms I would encourage you to seek help. Hormone Replacement Therapy (HRT) has historically received a bad press because

of its alleged link with breast cancer but examination of the studies has shown that the original research findings were not reported in an accurate way. As long as a woman is assessed by a specialist, many women can receive HRT safely and benefit hugely from it. Many surgeries have a designated clinician who has a specialist interest in the menopause and will be best placed to give you individually tailored advice, which takes into account any relevant medical history. See:
www.nhs.uk/conditions/menopause

References

1. *Diagnostic and Statistical Manual of Mental Disorders, Fifth Edition* (Washington, USA: American Psychiatric Association, 2013)

CHAPTER SIX

Erectile Dysfunction

E rectile dysfunction (ED) is defined as "the persistent inability of a man to attain or sustain an erection for satisfactory sexual activity."[1] It affects more than 152 million men worldwide and that figure is predicted to rise to 300 million by the year 2025.[2] Most men occasionally fail to get or keep an erection, because of stress, tiredness, anxiety or too much alcohol. This is nothing to worry about, but persistent ED can continue for many months or years.

Until the late 1990s, it was believed that ED was primarily caused by psychological issues, but further research has shown the causes for many men are likely to be physical. If the causes are thought to be physical, then the ED is referred to as organic. If the causes are thought to be psychological, then the ED is referred to as psychogenic. For some men, it is thought their ED is the result of a combination of organic and psychogenic causes. The most common cause of organic ED is atherosclerosis, a disease that causes the "furring up" of the blood vessels, including those that supply blood to the penis.[3, 4]

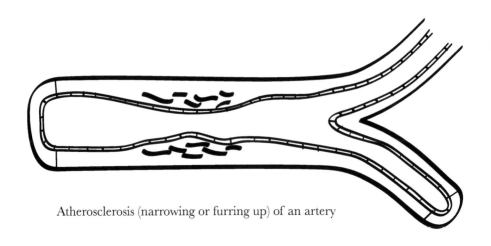

Atherosclerosis (narrowing or furring up) of an artery

This furring up process can also clog the heart arteries and cause cardiovascular disease (CVD). Discovering this has been a significant advance, because we now know that if a man presents with ED and is diagnosed with a vascular disease, then he has a fifty-fold increased risk of developing heart disease in the following ten years, compared with a man who does not have ED.[5] ED can be an early warning sign of future heart problems, appearing some three to five years before a heart complaint, so a man will get "symptoms" in his penis before his heart. So, if he sees his doctor for treatment soon after his ED starts, he may be able to prevent future medical conditions, including heart problems.

An interesting theory called the "artery size" hypothesis explains the link between ED and CVD.[6] The body is like a tree and it has a network of arteries supplying blood to all the organs. Some branches are bigger than others, e.g. those supplying the heart and the head, and some are smaller branches, such as those supplying the penis. Atherosclerosis affects the whole vascular system (tree), but symptoms rarely appear simultaneously. A narrowing in a small artery such as the penile artery (1-2mm) will cause symptoms much quicker than a narrowing in the heart artery, which is about 3-4mm in diameter.

If you have ED you *must* see your GP, not only to discuss this but to undergo an assessment and health screen to rule out more serious illnesses such as diabetes and heart disease.

ED can have devastating consequences, impacting self-esteem, work, and family relationships, as the following statements, taken from anonymous questionnaires, show:

- "This has been a terrible worry – my wife feels it is a reflection on her."

- "It's caused huge problems in my relationship and had a huge impact on my quality of life."

- "I feel devastated by this."

- "My partner has said that she will leave me if I don't sort this problem out, and then I couldn't go on living."

- "I feel as if I have let my wife down."

Men may be reluctant to talk about their ED, so often don't realise how common it is. A 2003 survey showed that nearly 50 percent of ED sufferers took almost two years to seek professional help.[7]

Is the ED situational or absolute?

Some useful questions to consider the causes of ED are:

- Are you still experiencing strong night-time or morning erections?

If a man still experiences night-time and early morning erections, which are nothing to do with sexual stimulation or arousal, this would indicate the arteries are working normally. Night-time erections are the body's way of keeping the *corpora cavernosa* (spongy tissue) in the penis well oxygenated with blood. Men have eight times more blood in the penis when they have an erection compared with when the penis is flaccid (soft), so it is important that the arteries supplying the tissues are able to fully dilate and allow this surge of blood. Atherosclerosis has a two-fold disadvantage: the ability of the blood vessels to dilate is impaired and the artery is narrower because of "furring up."

> 🖉 Are you able to get a good erection if you are on your own and stimulate yourself?

If the answer is "Yes" to both these questions, then the ED is more likely to be situational. This suggests that the blood supply to the penis is good. The plumbing system is working as it should and the erection problems are more likely to have an underlying psychological cause.

If the answer to one or both of these questions is "No", then the ED may have an underlying physical cause. If there is a problem with penile blood flow, regardless of the situation and other external factors, then we would describe this as being absolute.

Some men can find a psychogenic diagnosis helpful as they can then focus on why some situations pose a problem and others don't. Other men don't find this diagnosis reassuring and if the ED does not have an underlying organic cause, they are left with more questions than answers: "If the ED is psychological, do I have a mental health problem?" "How can the ED be treated?" "If it's all in my head, will I ever be able to have a good erection again?"

The diagnosis of ED is not a black and white science and there could be a mixed diagnosis of psychological and physical factors, but these simple considerations can help build up a picture of what is happening. Considering predisposing, precipitating, and maintaining factors for the ED can also give us a clearer idea of whether we think the ED is physical, psychological or a mixture of the two.

Predisposing factors

As well as the usual questions we would cover in predisposing factors, we might particularly be interested in a man's general health, medication, relationship issues, and past sexual experiences. Some men have struggled with ED from their very first sexual experience. Perhaps they attempted intercourse with a partner, lost their erection, and were taunted. This may have haunted them ever since, in every relationship. Or perhaps a man grew up in a family or culture where sex was only about procreation, or he has inhibitions over contraception. Many people have not had adequate sex education and this creates a pattern of unrealistic expectations. Those who have watched a lot of pornography may have unrealistic expectations about sex, or may need a much increased level of stimulation to promote arousal. Real sexual experience with their wives is not enough to stimulate or maintain an erection (see Chapter 4 on the damaging effects of pornography).

Precipitating (triggering) factors

Has there been a trigger for the ED? This could be a physical or psychological cause.

Physical causes

Men whose ED is due to physical causes often experience a gradual onset of erectile problems. This tends to be absolute rather than situational. As we have seen, if the ED is absolute then the man is likely to notice a reduction or absence altogether of morning and night-time erections, and difficulty getting or maintaining an erection when he is with his partner or if he stimulates himself. The list below is not exhaustive but it will give you a good idea of some of the physical causes of ED:

- vasculogenic conditions (which affect blood flow to the penis) including atherosclerosis, cardiovascular disease (CVD), hypertension (high blood pressure), and raised cholesterol

- neurogenic conditions (which affect the nervous system) including multiple sclerosis, Parkinson's disease, stroke, diabetes, and spinal injury

- hormonal conditions – an overactive/underactive thyroid gland, hypogonadism (low testosterone levels), a head or brain trauma, or radiation to the head

- anatomical conditions (which affect the structure of the penis) including Peyronie's disease (a condition that can cause the penis to develop a curvature; see Appendix 2)

- surgery and radiation therapy for bladder, prostate or rectal cancer

- injury or trauma to the penis

- side effects of prescribed drugs, including medication to treat high blood pressure and antidepressants

- recreational drug use

- excessive alcohol consumption.

ED is also more likely to occur in people who smoke, are overweight, and are considered physically unfit.

There is some evidence that ED can be caused by prolonged periods of bicycle riding.[8] If you ride a bike for more than three hours a week and you are experiencing ED, your doctor may recommend you try a period without cycling to see if this improves things. Make sure you are sitting in the correct position with a properly fitted, comfortable seat – some cycle saddles are specifically designed to relieve pressure on the blood vessels and nerves supplying the penis.

Psychological causes

A psychological cause of ED is more likely if:

- Your erection is fine except when you try to have penetrative sex with your partner

- You are suffering stress and anxiety

- You and/or your spouse are unhappy in the marriage

- You are depressed

- You are experiencing performance anxiety (see below) – you have "failed" once and you are fearful of subsequent failure

- Your partner has sexual problems: vaginismus, dyspareunia or low desire

- You are not sufficiently sexually aroused

Psychological ED is more likely to be described as situational. There is no underlying physical reason impairing blood flow to the penis, and erections often continue to occur during the night and when the man stimulates himself.

Performance anxiety

Performance anxiety, as we have seen, means the man worries about getting or keeping an erection, and this fear makes the situation worse. If the man has anxiety symptoms when attempting sex – an increased heart rate, sweaty palms, butterflies in the stomach, and so on – then this adrenaline response, produced by the body, may be affecting the erection. When a man has an erection the blood vessels need to dilate, and the counter-response of the hormone adrenaline, which caused the arteries to narrow, can hinder that response. A short course of drug treatment (see first-line treatments later in the chapter) can override the adrenaline response and enable good penile blood flow. Using a drug treatment can build a man's/couple's confidence. This is best done in combination with sex therapy, as it is important to encourage the couple to look at emotional and behavioural factors to reduce anxiety longer term. Then the man can wean himself off the drug treatment once the relevant inhibiting factors have been addressed and he has built up confidence.

Maintaining factors

Many things can perpetuate ED, such as on-going treatment for something like prostate cancer, fear of sex after a heart attack, or heart surgery. Marriage difficulties, different attitudes to sexual intimacy, or different levels of desire can also contribute. Perhaps a couple have waited until they were married to have sex and then the husband loses his erection. Both are disappointed but unable to talk about it. Further attempts at sex have the same result, and the silence continues.

When should you seek help?

If you have been experiencing ED, even for a short time, you need to seek help. It could be an early warning sign of a more serious underlying disease, as we have seen, such as cardiac disease or diabetes. Even if the cause is purely psychological, seek help in order to rule out physical causes and discuss treatment options.

Treatment for ED

As well as asking about your lifestyle and other factors, your GP will want to carry out a general health screen. This should include:

- heart and lungs
- blood pressure
- genitals, to rule out any obvious physical abnormality
- cholesterol blood level
- diabetes test
- a morning check of your testosterone blood level

If you have symptoms of an enlarged prostate gland, such as a weak urine stream and/or urgent or frequent urination, your doctor may also want to examine your prostate. (This is done by inserting a gloved finger into your rectum to feel the size and shape of the prostate gland.)

Treating ED involves tackling the cause of the problem, whether this is physical, psychological or a mixture of the two. There have been major advances in the treatment of ED in the last fifteen years, with the introduction of tablets that improve blood flow specifically to the penis. Most men can be treated effectively with these.

Often tablets will be the first-line treatment, whether the cause is thought to be physical or psychological. The main difference is that if the cause is thought to be psychological then couples can benefit from a combined approach to treatment, which includes tablets and also sex therapy. This is particularly important when a man has experienced lifelong sexual problems or the ED has caused tension within the marriage.

Addressing physical causes

If atherosclerosis is causing your ED, your doctor will want to ensure that this condition is managed appropriately, to reduce the chance of cardiac disease and other health-related complications, such as high blood pressure or stroke. Your doctor may prescribe medications to treat atherosclerosis (such as cholesterol-lowering medication and drugs to lower your blood pressure). Some lifestyle changes may also be recommended to improve your general health and help protect your heart and blood vessels. These may include stopping smoking, limiting the amount of alcohol you drink, losing weight if you are overweight, taking daily exercise, and trying to reduce stress and anxiety.

If your GP has any concerns about your heart, particularly whether it is safe for you to have sex, they will refer you for further investigation with a cardiologist (heart doctor). They may, therefore, defer treating your ED until they are sure that sexual intercourse won't endanger your heart.

However, there is only a small degree of cardiac risk associated with sexual intercourse. Sexual activity makes the same physiological demands on the heart as mild to moderate exercise, similar to other aspects of normal daily life, such as walking a mile on flat ground in 20 minutes, or 15 minutes of housework or gardening.[9]

If you have already been diagnosed with heart disease, diabetes, or high blood pressure, then it will be important for you to be adequately assessed to determine any cardiac risk. Most patients will be deemed low cardiac risk and can receive treatment for their ED immediately. If a patient is deemed to be intermediate risk (having three or more cardiac risk factors) or high risk (displaying symptoms such as angina or increased shortness of breath when walking upstairs, doing housework or gardening), then they would need to defer treatment to have further investigation and stabilisation, prior to drug treatment.[3, 10]

When Viagra® was introduced in 1998, many men with ED started to take it, unprescribed, via the internet. Some were undiagnosed cardiac "time bombs" – their ED was an early warning sign of the furring up of their arteries, and having sex precipitated heart attacks and, in some cases, death. Viagra® was then blamed, in the media, but it is important to stress that drugs for ED do not cause heart disease. It is the sexual activity in an undiagnosed man that increases the risk of a heart attack, not the drug.

Drug treatments

The treatments for ED can be divided into first-line treatment (tablets) and second-line treatment (non-oral). Tablets have been shown to be both safe and effective for many men, and I will concentrate on these. I will also list second-line treatments, but in almost all cases, your GP would prescribe tablets as a first option. In some exceptional cases, contra-indicating medication or a medical condition may preclude a patient from having oral treatment but these cases are fairly rare and this would be something your GP would discuss with you.

First-line treatment

Tablets

These will include the use of a family of drugs called phosphodiesterase inhibitors (PDE5i). These include Tadalafil (Cialis®), Vardenafil (Levitra®), Sildenafil (Viagra®), and Avanafil (Spedra®). Sildenafil is also sold as a generic drug. PDE5i are a very effective group of drugs. They are not aphrodisiacs and do not increase sexual desire. They work by relaxing the blood vessels in the penis, allowing blood to flow into it, causing an erection. This would not be a spontaneous erection; the man has to be mentally and physically aroused. This is vital for couples because it replicates what would "normally" be happening. Consequently, the partner still feels very much part of the arousal process, as they would do were drugs unnecessary. If a man has normal erectile function, he should not take a PDE5i. These drugs are safe for couples trying to conceive, but in such a case, this should be discussed with the GP or specialist first.

Men with psychological ED usually only take tablets for a limited period of time. This could be around six to twelve months, to get over any performance anxiety. Those with an underlying physical cause usually need the drugs for life, because the physical cause cannot be reversed.

Schedule 2 prescribing guidelines

As of 1 July 1999 the British government introduced guidelines as to who could receive drug treatment on the NHS and who would have to pay for their treatment. When I say "pay" I do not mean the cost of a standard prescription but the actual cost of the drug, and this is regardless of age or ability to pay. You can find more about the Schedule 2 prescribing guidelines in Appendix 1.

The cost of tablets for erectile dysfunction

Most men have to pay for their ED tablets. The GP or medical specialist can provide you with a private prescription. You should not be charged for the prescription to be written (for other medicines the prescribing doctor can make a charge), but you will be required to pay for the cost of the tablet. It is important to note that some pharmacies will include an administration charge for dispensing the private prescription on top of the cost of the drugs, so it is really worth shopping around for your tablets.

Many of the pharmacies within supermarkets supply ED drugs at very competitive prices, as do online pharmacies such as Pharmacy 2U (this is a well-respected online pharmacy, used by the NHS. I would be cautious about using other online pharmacies). In 2013 Viagra® (trade name for Sildenafil) was taken off patent so it can be bought at a much lower cost and is now sold as Sildenafil. Historically a patient might pay anywhere from £6 to £12 a tablet depending on the dose. Sildenafil (the same ingredient) can be bought for as little as 85p per tablet.

If you are receiving treatment on the NHS because you come under one of the specialist groups covered in the guidelines, you may well be automatically prescribed Sildenafil because it is by far the cheapest option. You may want to read about the other treatment options though, such as Tadalafil. It will be up to you to negotiate with your GP or prescribing clinician which drug you think would suit you best.

The main difference between Sildenafil and Vardenafil versus Tadalafil is the duration of action – how long the drug stays actively working in the body. Sildenafil, Viagra® and Levitra are licensed to work for up to four hours, whereas Tadalafil has a longer duration of action, up to 36 hours. Tadalafil can also be taken as a daily dose which means a man is covered at all times should he be sufficiently stimulated and want to get an erection. If Tadalafil is taken as a daily dose the man has to take the drug for five consecutive days before the drug will have reached its optimal therapeutic level in the body. The drug then needs to be taken daily to maintain this dose in the body.

The pharmaceutical companies can all show you research which "proves" their drug is the best. In my experience working with patients, all of the drugs are very effective (I cannot comment on the newer drug Spedra because I have never used this with a patient). Most of my patients have chosen to use Tadalafil long term, because of its longer duration of action, which means they can relax, knowing they have a 36-hour "window" in which to have sexual intimacy. This feels far less pressured than the much shorter window provided by the other drugs.

My advice is to try each drug and see how you get on. You must try each drug at least eight to twelve times consecutively before you make a decision about it, and many men try all of them, over many months, before settling on the one they wish to use long term. Above all, though, get yourself medically assessed, by your GP or a specialist, before you take an oral drug for ED. Don't use an online doctor, and don't buy drugs from anywhere other than a reputable pharmacy. Counterfeit drugs for ED are a huge, very profitable, illegal business. Taking them is dangerous: you won't know what is in them, and often they simply cost you money but don't actually work.

Your GP or specialist will discuss possible side effects with you. These are rare and usually transient. Persist with the drug, if the side effects are tolerable, as usually they wear off with time. Common side effects with PDE5 inhibitors are: facial flushing, headaches, nasal stuffiness, and occasionally stomach irritation. If these persist and are troubling, discuss alternative treatments.

Second-line treatments

If tablets don't work for you, or you cannot take them, then second-line treatment options will be discussed with you. Further information about these can be found in Appendix 1.

Does age affect your treatment?

ED is more common as men get older (because of the increased incidence of other diseases such as high blood pressure and raised cholesterol) but men in their nineties can still receive treatment to enable them to enjoy sexual intimacy with their partners. While some older men and their partners accept loss of erectile function as a normal part of ageing and do not want treatment, others are unhappy about losing such an important part of their lives. It is perfectly normal for men and women to continue an active sex life well into older age and no one should be denied treatment for ED on the grounds of age.

Conclusion

Erectile dysfunction is very common and can be an early warning sign of other serious diseases. Any man experiencing ED should have a check-up with his GP and then consider treatment options. Even if you are not currently sexually active you should still see your GP for a health screen, if you think you have ED. This will build up your confidence and assurance that you can have a fulfilling sex life in the future if you choose. Oral treatments for ED are simple, easy to take, and very effective, so don't suffer in silence.

Finally, the Bible verses below remind us of the joy of being part of an intimate team, and the privilege of entering into this unique partnership with our spouse, especially when we face challenges or difficulties. We are also reminded that we are not alone but as Christians there are three strands to this unique bond, with God at the centre.

Two are better than one, for they have a good return for their work: if either of them falls down, one can help the other up. But pity anyone who falls and has no one to help them up! Also, if two lie down together, they will keep warm. But how can one keep warm alone? Though one may be overpowered, two can defend themselves. A cord of three strands is not quickly broken.

Ecclesiastes 4:9–12

References

1. Feldman, H. A., Goldstein, I., Hatzichristou, D. G., et al. (1994) Impotence and its medical and psychosocial correlates: results of the Massachusetts Male Aging Study. *Journal of Urology*, 151, 54–61.

2. Aytac, I., Mckindlay, J., Krane, R. (1999) The likely worldwide increase in erectile dysfunction between 1995 and 2025 and some possible policy consequences. *British Journal of Urology International*, 84, 50–6.

3. Jackson, G., Betteridge, J., Dean, J., et al. (2002) A systematic approach to erectile dysfunction in the cardiovascular patient: a consensus statement update. *International Journal of Clinical Practice*, 56, 633–71.

4. Bortolotti, A., Parazzini, F., Colli, E., et al. (1997) The epidemiology of erectile dysfunction and its risk factors. *International Journal of Andrology*, 20, 323–34.

5. Chew, K. K., Finn, J., Stuckey, B., et al. (2010) Erectile dysfunction as a predictor for subsequent atherosclerotic cardiovascular events: findings from a linked-data study. *Journal of Sexual Medicine*, 7, 192-202.

6. Montorsi, P., Montorsi, F., Schulman, C. (2003) Is erectile dysfunction the tip of the iceberg of a systemic vascular disorder? *European Journal of Urology*, 44, 352–54.

7. *Private parts, public policy: improving men's sexual health*: a report by the Men's Health forum, London, 2003.

8. Huang, V., Munarriz, R., et al. (2005) Bicycle riding and erectile dysfunction: an increase in interest (and concern). *Journal of Sexual Medicine*, 2, 596–604.

9. Muller, J., Ahlbom, A., et al. (2001) Sexual activity as a trigger of myocardial infarction: a case cross-over analysis in the Stockholm Heart Epidemiology Programme (SHEEP). *Heart.* 86, 387–90.

10. Kostis, J. B., Jackson, G., Rosen, R., et al. (2005) Sexual dysfunction and cardiac risk (the Second Princeton Consensus Conference). *American Journal of Cardiology*, 96, (2), 313–21.

CHAPTER SEVEN

Vaginismus

*'Come to me, all you who are weary and burdened, and I will
give you rest. Take my yoke upon you and learn from me, for I am
gentle and humble in heart, and you will find rest for your souls.
For my yoke is easy and my burden is light.'*

Matthew 11:28–30

Vaginismus (difficulties with vaginal penetration) and dyspareunia (painful sex) are the most common causes of unconsummated marriage (a couple who have not been able to engage in full penetrative sexual intercourse). A collective term for these symptoms is Genito-Pelvic Pain/Penetration Disorder (GPPPD). Symptoms of vaginismus and dyspareunia often overlap but not always. Both conditions result in anxiety and often avoidance of sex. It is worth familiarising yourself with the term GPPPD because you may hear this term mentioned if you visit your GP or hospital specialist. For the purposes of this book I have provided separate chapters for vaginismus and dyspareunia.

Diagnosis

For a diagnosis of vaginismus/GPPPD to be made, there needs to be a persistence of one or more of the following symptoms:

- difficulty with vaginal penetration during sexual intercourse

- marked genital or pelvic pain during attempts at intercourse

- significant fear of pain as a result of vaginal penetration

- tensing or tightening of the pelvic floor muscles, which makes attempted vaginal penetration difficult, if not impossible

This vaginal tightness results from the involuntary tightening of the pelvic floor, especially that of the pubococcygeus (PC) muscle group. Many women are not aware that this is the usual cause and ask if the problems are simply in their head. It is like being anxious – the anxiety starts in our minds, but it has physical manifestations. These can include a pounding heart and a dry mouth: in vaginismus, this is the involuntary spasm of the PC muscles. It is the body's way of protecting itself, even if the woman does not understand the need for protection.

Impossible Penetration

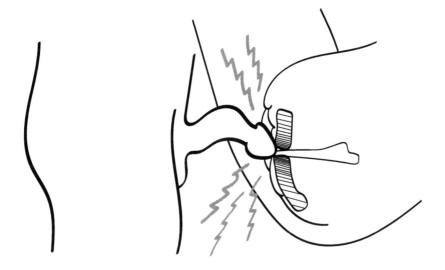

As intercourse is attempted, the PC muscle group (darkly shaded) involuntarily tightens the vaginal entrance, making intercourse impossible.

Tightness and Pain

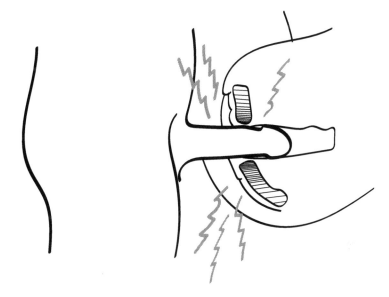

In other cases of vaginismus, penetration may be possible, but the woman experiences periods of involuntary tightness causing burning, discomfort, or pain.

Further diagnostic criteria require that the difficulties:

- need to have lasted for around six months
- cause significant distress
- cannot be better explained by another mental health disorder
- do not result from severe relationship distress or breakdown
- do not result from another external stress such as sudden trauma
- cannot be attributed to the effects of substances/medication taken, or another medical condition

So, for example, if a woman is undergoing radiotherapy for cervical cancer, it would be normal for her to have many of the symptoms listed above, in the recovery phase. It would also be normal to experience pain after a difficult childbirth. But a woman might be diagnosed with vaginismus if penetrative sex was still painful after a suitable recovery period had passed. I would suggest waiting six months and if the symptoms have not improved, then I would encourage a woman to see her GP.

Research suggests that the prevalence of vaginismus ranges from 4-6 percent.[1] Often women first seek help when they want to start a family. Of those I see in my clinic, most have not embarked on a sexual relationship before marriage, for religious or cultural reasons. I suspect the problem is more widespread than estimated. And while I believe that penetrative sex is an important part of sexual intimacy, it is also possible to have a very active and satisfying sexual relationship without it. But if vaginismus is a problem, repeated failed attempts to make love can result in a non-sexual marriage. It can be an extremely distressing condition for both the man and woman and is not widely discussed.

Treatment plan

If you suspect that you may have vaginismus, it is important that you visit your GP. They will be interested in your general health, your relationship, and they will also want to ask some more specific questions.

Is the vaginismus primary or secondary?

Primary vaginismus means you have always had this problem: secondary means you have been able to take vaginal penetration in the past but now something has happened to change this. Most unconsummated marriages are the result of primary vaginismus.

Is the vaginismus situational or absolute?

- Can you use a tampon?
- Have you been able to have a smear test?

🌿 Have you had penetrative sex with other partners in the past?

🌿 Can a finger be inserted into your vagina?

If the answer to any of these questions is "Yes", then the vaginismus would be considered situational, i.e. there are some situations where vaginal penetration can be tolerated and others where it cannot. Situational vaginismus can provide clues to what is causing it. However, if the answer to all the above questions is "no" then this means the woman has absolute vaginismus.

Your GP will almost certainly want you to have a physical examination, which can be performed by themselves or by a gynaecologist. It may seem odd, given the condition, to insist upon a physical examination, but it is important to rule out any other medical condition, such as endometriosis or anatomical abnormalities. Gynaecologists who are used to working with this condition can usually perform an internal examination with relatively little distress to the patient.

Gynaecologists who specialise in vaginismus may be available and you may be able to ask to see someone specific, if your GP is happy to fund this. Once you have a diagnosis of vaginismus, you have a couple of options. You can be referred to a psychosexual therapist on the NHS, though there has been a reduction in NHS-funded clinics and waiting lists in some areas can be long. You can find your own therapist (see Chapter 5) or you can undertake a self-help programme of your own with your husband.

Here are some criteria that might help you both decide which of these routes to take:

🌿 Have either of you experienced any form of sexual trauma or sex abuse?

- Is the vaginismus creating tension between you and your husband?

- Is the vaginismus causing either of you high levels of distress, anxiety or depression?

- Has the marriage become "sexless", i.e. you have completely stopped engaging in any form of sexual intimacy?

If you answer "Yes" to any of these questions then I would advise you to find a therapist who is used to working with this condition. You may need more support than you would get from working as a couple alone. Not being able to consummate a marriage can drive a wedge between a couple, and in such a case, a therapist may want to do some initial relational work with you before they embark on a self-help programme. Maintaining the intimate team is possible at this time, though some couples need help to do so. Learning strategies to do so will stand you in good stead for any sexual or relationship difficulties you may face in the future. For some people, the underlying cause of vaginismus can be sexual abuse or trauma. Discussing such issues can be immensely painful, but it can be done, taking time and patience.

Self-focused couple work

There will be five parts to completing the self-focused couple work:

1. The woman (and man if he wishes) will need to undertake a personal/sexual growth programme

2. The woman needs to be comfortable with a finger being inserted fully into the vagina (either her finger and/or her partner's)

3. She needs to become comfortable inserting a graduating set of vaginal dilators

4. She needs to be able to allow the penis to be fully inserted into the vagina (this is called vaginal containment)

5. She needs to allow the penis to be moved back and forth within the vagina comfortably, enabling ejaculation and orgasm (possibly mutual)

It is not uncommon for couples with vaginismus to find the man can start to develop sexual difficulties of his own, most commonly erectile dysfunction (ED) or premature ejaculation (PE) and I have covered these issues in other chapters.

If you are planning on undertaking self-focused couple work, you need to be able to agree with the following statements:

⌀ I have undergone a physical examination and there is no physical abnormality or other medical condition preventing vaginal penetration

⌀ As a couple, although we cannot engage in penetrative sex, we can enjoy intimate sexual contact

⌀ We are committed to working together as a couple and we work well as an intimate team

The work that you will be doing as a couple will replicate what you would have done with a therapist, so you will need to look to each other for support and encouragement.

Self-focused couple work – a five-step programme

Before I go on to outline the five-step couple programme, I am going to give you some important information about vaginal lubricants; these will be necessary as you move through the steps.

Vaginal lubricants

You will need to use lots and lots of lubrication when undertaking the five-step couple programme and particularly using vaginal dilators. I cannot stress this enough. If you are inserting a finger then you can use any type of lubricant. When you move on to using a vaginal dilator you will need to ensure the lubricant you use is compatible with the dilator. If the dilator is plastic then you can use a silicone, oil or water-based lubricant. If the dilators are made of silicone, the lubricant will need to be water-based. Do perform a patch test on your forearm to ensure you will not have any sort of adverse allergic reaction when using a lubricant on your genital area.

When a woman is sexually aroused the vagina naturally produces lubrication, but we cannot expect this to happen when inserting a finger or dilator into the vagina, at least not when using them initially. In the early stages, the exercises are not likely to feel arousing but rather exploratory. This can change when the couple start using them together as part of sexual intimacy and the focus may include arousal. Apply whatever lubricant you use liberally, to the vulval area and inside the vagina. You need to create a gliding feel. Avoid lubricants designed to increase arousal through tingling or heat. See Appendix 3 for more information.

How long and how often for each step?

It would not be helpful to be prescriptive about how many times you do each step of the programme before you move on to the next. Every woman will be different. Some may find one particular step straightforward and move through it quickly with ease but find another step more challenging. A general rule of thumb is that you need to be able to complete the exercise with relative ease before moving on to the next step. Exercises can take anywhere from twenty minutes to 45 minutes, depending which step you are on, whether you are working on your own or with your spouse, and how easy or challenging you are finding the steps.

If I am working with a woman or couple, I usually leave a two-week interval between appointments, and you might want to do the same. It is important that you work out how much time you can commit to completing the exercises for each particular stage and then stick to this. Ideally you will complete these two to three times a week. For my clients, this would mean that, by the time I see the woman again, she has usually completed each step four to six times, and she is relatively confident about her ability to move on to the next step.

Sometimes a woman comes back and she has not completed the exercise at all. There will be reasons: illness, having her period, perhaps travelling – all can make it more difficult to complete the exercises. This is why it is important you only embark on the programme when you have a couple of months when you can devote time to it.

On other occasions, however, a woman repeatedly finds reasons not to complete the exercises and I will gently challenge what is going on, and discuss some of the barriers she is listing. Very often a delay is down to fear, which is quite understandable. If the fear is overwhelming, then we may agree to suspend the programme and spend a couple of sessions focusing on anxiety before we move back to the practical steps.

Once you have mastered each step, you can move on to the next. You may find one step is very easy and you only spend two or three sessions on it, maybe just a week, and then you move on to the next. You may, however, need to spend three or four weeks on another step before you feel ready to move on. That's fine. Remember you are moving closer to your goal with each step.

Step 1

Most women, and this includes women who do not have vaginismus, have never looked at their vulval area. Go back and read Chapter 2 and follow all the exploratory advice there.

Step 2

This will involve you becoming comfortable inserting a finger fully into the vagina. Once you feel comfortable inserting your own finger into your vagina, you may feel confident enough for your husband to try inserting his finger.

To do this, you should adopt a comfortable reclined position. Your vulval area should be well lubricated and at this point it is worth applying more lubrication to your forefinger or index finger. To begin with, I suggest you insert your own finger so you retain full control over the process. As you insert a finger into your vagina you will probably feel resistance. Hold your hand still (when it comes to involving your husband you will need to ask him to hold his hand still) and don't be tempted to pull it out. Take three or four deep breaths, breathing in through your nose, expanding your chest and then slowly breathing out of your mouth. Concentrate on the sensation of breathing. After doing this, you should find you are slightly more relaxed and can insert your/his finger a little further. Do not be disheartened if you struggle at first; it will become easier the more you do it. If you are struggling or beginning to feel pain (not simply discomfort), then stop and either give yourself a few minutes to relax and try again, or plan to have another go at the next scheduled time later that week.

Many people, as we saw in Chapter 2, believe that the vagina is a hollow tunnel inside the woman, but this is not the case. When you insert your finger you will feel the vaginal muscles (like two cushions), and you will feel your finger sliding between these cushions. Vaginal penetration is so pleasurable for men because the penis is stimulated by the feel of the vaginal muscles surrounding it. God has designed us very cleverly. Women have a greater concentration of nerve endings in the lower third of the vagina, and these often provide pleasurable sensations when stimulated during sexual activity.

When it comes to involving your husband in Step 2, you will feel more comfortable if you are in control of the process. To do this, ensure you are propped up on a couple of cushions so that you can see what he is doing. Ask him to lie next to you or sit between your legs. It will be important for you to communicate clearly with him, and having eye contact will aid this. It is really important that both your vulval area and vagina are well lubricated, as is your husband's finger. It is probably going to be easiest if he uses his forefinger or his index (middle) finger. Ideally you would spend some time as a couple touching your vulval and clitoral area first, because many women will find this process arousing, which will further aid enjoyment and your body's own ability to produce lubrication. It is very important as you do this that you continue to tell him what feels nice and if possible guide his hand or finger to areas you feel are particularly sensual or arousing. Take your time and pace yourselves. You may take three or four sessions before you feel confident to attempt any sort of vaginal penetration, but that is the aim – that either you or he can fully insert one finger into the vagina.

Some patients are not able to insert a finger into their vagina, yet quickly make progress with the smallest finer-sized dilator. You will need to judge as a couple what works for you.

Step 3

Vaginal dilators are cone-shaped devices graduated in size and designed to be gently inserted into the vagina. This enables the woman to feel that she is gradually gaining some sense of control over vaginal penetration. Over time she will notice that her PC muscles are relaxing and insertion of the graduated sizes becomes easier. Some women do not like using dilators and prefer to use different-sized vibrators. These can feel less clinical and can also be used to increase sexual arousal at the same time. Appendix 3 has more information. For the purposes of this chapter, I will use the word "dilator" but this also includes vibrators. There are a number of vaginal dilator kits available on the market.

Carefully consider when you are going to use the dilators. Don't try to squeeze this between other commitments. I suggest scheduling time, perhaps 45 minutes, to enjoy the experience of preparation and then fifteen to twenty minutes completing the exercise. Use candles to soften the lighting, put relaxing music on, and perhaps have a glass of wine. Make sure that if you are taking alcohol this is done in moderation and you are fully in control and engaged in the sensations you are experiencing. Being intoxicated would be detrimental to the process. Make sure you always work through Step 1 before inserting the dilator so that your body is as relaxed and prepared as possible. It can take two to three months for the process of using the dilators to work, so I suggest finding that period of time, and make sure your schedule can accommodate that.

The recommended position to use the dilators is to lie flat on your back with your knees bent and legs slightly apart, or slightly propped up on the bed with cushions. Some women prefer to stand with one leg raised on the bed or a chair. When first using the dilators, you may find you can only tolerate the tip. When transitioning sizes, move from the smaller dilator to the next size in the same session, as vaginal muscles will already be relaxed and the transition will be easier.

It is important to be able to do the exercises at least twice a week, and you may want to look at novel ways of incorporating the exercises into intimate time as a couple. Work with your body's natural sexual arousal as this will aid the process of inserting the dilators.

Just as a man gets an erection (and as a result eight times more blood flows into the penis) so when a woman becomes aroused, the blood vessels in her genitals dilate (see Chapter 2 for the female arousal model). There is increased blood flow in the vaginal walls, which causes fluid to pass through them. This is the main source of lubrication, which makes the vagina wet. The external genitalia or vulva (including the clitoris, vaginal opening, and inner and outer lips or labia) become engorged (swollen) due to the increased blood supply. Inside the body, the top of the vagina expands in preparation for vaginal penetration. This can be using the dilators at this stage and then it will be the penis when you move on to the final stage of the programme.

When using the dilators, a woman should hold them herself to start with, so she has full control over the sensations and can respond to what she is feeling. Once she is more confident, she can ask her partner to take over this process, on the explicit understanding that he listens to her feedback and goes at a pace led by her. This can be hugely unifying, and an important way of involving the partner. This can, for some couples, be a very sexually arousing experience.

As you insert the dilator, you will probably feel resistance, as you did initially when trying to insert a finger. Hold the dilator still (don't be tempted to pull it out) and, in the same way, take three or four deep breaths, breathing in through your nose, expanding your chest, and then slowly breathing out of your mouth. Concentrate on the sensation of breathing. After doing this, you should find you are slightly more relaxed and can insert the dilator a little further. Do not be disheartened if you struggle at first; it will become easier the more you do it. If you are struggling or beginning to feel pain (not simply discomfort) then stop and either give yourself a few minutes to relax and try again, or plan to have another go at the next scheduled time later that week.

At this point, lots of women say the dilator simply will not go in. Their body feels like a brick wall. With time and patience, however, you will notice that the pelvic floor muscles slowly start to relax and gradual penetration is possible. Once you have become comfortable with the smallest dilator and can insert it easily, move up to the next size.

When you are using the dilators with your husband, you might like to kiss, or ask him to touch your breasts or other sensual areas, such as the inner thighs, to help relax or arouse you. You may already experience clitoral orgasms through the use of a vibrator, self-touching or stimulation by your partner. When a woman has an orgasm, blood flow to the lower third of the vagina reaches its limit and causes the lower area of the vagina to become swollen and firm. If you are able to achieve an orgasm, this can hugely aid the process of penetration. You might like to experiment using the dilators after orgasm, when the vagina will be most engorged and padded, and you feel most lubricated and relaxed.

Step 4

When you have been able to move through the graduated dilators you will be ready to try to insert the penis into the vagina. Use lots of lubrication. One of the best positions is for the woman to sit over her husband's penis, facing him, while he lies on his back. This way she can ensure her husband remains still and she can gradually lower herself downwards over the penis. This position also enables her to feel in control of the pace at which she inserts the penis into her vagina.

One of the most important factors here is good communication between the couple. Try to ensure eye contact is made and both can talk about what they are experiencing. You may need to regularly stop (but not take the penis out) while you do your deep breathing exercises and then continue once you feel more relaxed. Once you are able to move your pelvis downwards so the penis is "contained" in the vagina, hold this position for a minute or so and then slowly move your body upwards (if you are in the superior position) and remove the penis from the vagina.

Step 5

You will need to complete Step 4 a couple of times before you move to full intercourse, when the penis can move freely in and out of the vagina. This will result in heightened arousal for the man and ultimately ejaculation and orgasm. At this point a couple have achieved full penetrative intercourse and then have officially consummated their marriage. As you get used to this sensation, you may find that one session is successful and another is not. Try not to be disheartened by this. Think how far you have come, if you have even reached this stage. It may be that you want to have a session where you just use the dilators again and then revisit the vaginal containment exercise.

When I see couples in the clinic who have achieved full intercourse, there is often such a feeling of achievement, I have been known to punch the air in celebration! It can be an emotional time for couples who have worked together over a long period of time to get to this point. But once they have finally achieved penetrative intercourse, it will not necessarily be plain sailing. They will possibly need to continue to use the dilators for a while, as they get used to the different sensations of penile penetration. They may also want to experiment with different sexual positions and techniques and I give more information on this in Chapter 3.

Contraception

Depending on your religious beliefs you may choose not to use any contraception, or you may choose Natural Fertility Planning (NFP), which is a method endorsed by the Catholic Church that enables couples to plan intimacy in order to plan for pregnancy or to postpone or avoid it.

You may choose to use hormonal or barrier contraception methods, and if so, it is important to think about what will work best for you as a couple whilst working towards consummating your marriage and getting comfortable with penetrative sex. Some couples find thinking about this difficult because they are desperate to conceive, but they equally recognise that they want a period of enjoying full intercourse prior to getting pregnant. Once pregnant, as we have seen earlier, a woman will go through huge hormonal changes and this can also influence how she feels about sex. Some women notice an increase in their libido during various points in the pregnancy. Typically this is in the second trimester (three to six months). Other women experience the opposite and notice a reduction in their libido.

Theoretically, assuming there are no fertility issues, you could get pregnant the first time you have penetrative sex. This might be very exciting for some couples, but others may feel they want to consolidate what they have been doing before they think about trying to conceive. Pregnancy is wonderful but it can potentially also create a whole set of other challenges related to what you might want to do sexually. There can be huge variation in how a woman feels about how her pregnant body is changing. Some women enjoy the changes and others do not. Men also vary hugely in how they feel about their wife during this phase. How a couple choose to approach this will be very individual, but what I would advocate is that you talk about this before you actively start having regular penetrative intercourse so you have a shared plan.

Conclusion

I have always believed that I cannot run. It has always resulted in me gasping for breath and feeling sick. About two years ago a friend of mine declared that she had recently taught herself to run five kilometres. It turns out that she "couldn't run" either, and described exactly the symptoms I had. I decided to take on the challenge…

The programme started off with baby steps, quite literally. After an initial warm-up, I ran for thirty seconds and then walked for five minutes, ran and then walked, and so on. I ran three times a week over the course of the next twelve weeks. I gradually ran five kilometres!

Some days I found it too hard and I gave up, feeling a bit dejected. Some days I had to stop halfway through, walk for a bit, and then resume the running when I felt able. Some days I amazed myself at being able to run for a whole minute and then gradually five minutes, eight minutes, twenty minutes, and finally thirty minutes. You may feel that the challenge of overcoming vaginismus is too difficult. Maybe you have lived with this problem for many years, and you believe that you are past being helped or indeed helping yourself. Maybe you feel sex will never be for you.

I had to equip myself with the right running kit. Likewise, you will need to invest some time in creating an environment that relaxes you, when you need to feel nurtured. You will need to decide whether you want to invest in a set of vaginal dilators or a selection of graduated vibrators, to experiment with different types of vaginal lubricants and think about what would help you to create a relaxing environment, such as soft lighting, scented candles, and music.

I had to plan the three days a week when I would keep up the running. I needed to create momentum; you will need to do the same. The two to three sessions a week to complete your self-focus, and then couple focus exercises, will not magically happen; you will need to prioritise these and ring fence that time, even if it means giving up something else.

Some days I had to stop. You will have days like this and you need to be kind to yourself and accept some days are just off-days, and prepare to try again at the next scheduled time.

I needed the support of my friend and my husband to encourage me when I felt I could not run, but ultimately they could not run for me. If you are unable to achieve your goal of sexual intercourse as a couple, perhaps you will need to invest in seeing a sex therapist. Some couples feel that seeing a therapist somehow negates the work they have done already. But a therapist can provide some much-needed support, encouragement, and that well deserved punch in the air when you do achieve your goal.

He gives strength to the weary and increases the power of the weak. Even youths grow tired and weary, and young men stumble and fall; but those who hope in the LORD will renew their strength. They will soar on wings like eagles; they will run and not grow weary, they will walk and not be faint.

Isaiah 40:29–31

References

1. Ter Kuile, M. Reissing, E. (2014). *Lifelong Vaginismus*. In Y.M. Binik & K. Hall (Eds), Principles and Practice of Sex Therapy (177-194). New York: Guildford Press.

CHAPTER EIGHT

Dyspareunia

Cast your cares on the LORD and he will sustain you;
he will never let the righteous be shaken.

Psalm 55:22

Pain felt during or after sex is known as dyspareunia. It is more common for women to experience sexual pain than men, and so women will be the focus of this chapter. I will address pain in men, which is relatively rare, at the end of the chapter.

Generally, I find that couples who have been unable to consummate their marriage will often present with vaginismus, whereas women who present with dyspareunia have often been able to have penetrative sex but it has been at least uncomfortable, if not painful. Consequently, the woman has become anxious and is less likely to become sexually aroused. This leads to further discomfort during sex and so a negative cycle is set up.

Diagnosis

Just to recap: for a diagnosis of dyspareunia/GPPPD to be made there needs to be persistence of one or more of the following symptoms:

- difficulty with vaginal penetration during sexual intercourse
- marked genital or pelvic pain during attempts at intercourse
- significant fear of pain as a result of vaginal penetration
- tensing or tightening of the pelvic floor muscles during attempted vaginal penetration which makes penetration difficult, if not impossible

Occasional dyspareunia is normal, with deep penetration for example, and is more likely at certain times during the woman's menstrual cycle. If it persists, preventing her from enjoying sexual intercourse, it may need treatment. Dyspareunia is common but rarely discussed. A large study of nearly seven thousand sexually active women aged 16 to 74 suggests that one in ten women experience pain during sex and sexual pain affects women of all ages. Women in their late fifties and early sixties are most likely to be affected (due to associated menopausal symptoms that will be discussed later in the chapter, along with treatments), followed by a younger group of women aged 16 to 24.[1]

Dyspareunia may be classified as superficial or deep. Superficial dyspareunia is pain experienced in the tissues around the entrance of the vagina. Deep dyspareunia is pain felt deeper within the pelvis on penetration or penile thrusting.

Primary or secondary?

Dyspareunia may have been present since a woman first started having sex, or attempted to use tampons, and this would be called primary dyspareunia. If it developed later in life after a period with no pain, it would be called secondary dyspareunia.

Situational or absolute?

Situational dyspareunia means the woman experiences pain in some situations but not others. For instance, she might be able to insert a tampon or vibrator into her vagina with no pain, but experiences pain when her partner inserts his penis. Absolute dyspareunia means she experiences pain with any type of vaginal penetration.

What causes dyspareunia?

It is not always easy to separate out what is a physical factor and what is a psychological or emotional factor when thinking about sexual pain. In order for a woman to enjoy sex, she needs to become aroused: this is her body's way of preparing itself for sexual intercourse. We considered in Chapter 2 what happens to a woman's body when she becomes sexually aroused.

If a woman is unable to become aroused then she may find sexual intercourse uncomfortable or painful. There may also be other psychological or emotional factors impacting how she responds to sexual intimacy – for instance, how she feels about the relationship. Both physical and emotional factors are important in dealing with dyspareunia and need to be considered during the assessment process. You might like to jot down things from the lists below that relate to you so you can start to build up your own picture of what the possible causes are.

Predisposing factors

These may have made it more likely you would find sexual intimacy painful and include:

- skin conditions affecting the vulva/vaginal entrance (e.g. eczema, Lichen sclerosis, Lichen planus)

- infectious conditions (e.g. frequent thrush, sexually transmitted infections, and urinary tract infections)

- structural problems causing obstruction (e.g. an abnormal hymen, a cyst or abscess, female circumcision, to name a few)

🍃 inflammatory conditions (e.g. pelvic inflammatory disease, endometriosis)

🍃 vulvovaginal atrophy (stiffening) and other symptoms associated with the menopause; changes in the lining of the vagina wall making the vagina more susceptible to irritation; discomfort and pain and reduced vaginal lubrication

🍃 some cancer treatments, which can cause some women to experience symptoms of an early menopause

🍃 radiotherapy for cancer in the pelvic region

🍃 muscular problems (e.g. vaginismus, spasm of the pelvic floor muscles)

🍃 reduction in vaginal lubrication, caused by hormonal changes, menopause, breastfeeding, stress, diabetes, use of antidepressants, to name just a few

🍃 reduction in or absence of vaginal lubrication, caused by a woman not being properly sexually aroused; this could be linked to emotional factors or because she is not finding the experience very enjoyable

As well as considering physical factors that might cause or contribute to sexual pain, I would also be interested in asking some more general questions about the state of the marital relationship.

Precipitating (triggering) factors and maintaining factors

I have combined these two factors, as a trigger will often maintain the pain if not addressed. If the dyspareunia is secondary then it would be useful to consider anything that happened just before the pain began, a precipitating factor. A trigger could be any number of things and I have listed some examples below:

- Have you developed a skin condition? This could be a result of an allergy to a new soap or washing powder

- Has your spouse started to use condoms? Could you have an allergy to the latex or spermicide in condoms?

- Have you started a new contraceptive?

- Are there obvious hormonal changes occurring such as the menopause?

- Have you started on any new medication that may affect vaginal lubrication?

- Have you undergone any treatment for cancer, such as surgery or radiotherapy to the pelvic area, or chemotherapy or endocrine therapy?

- Are you experiencing any anatomical or structural problems (e.g. injury/scarring from an episiotomy, trauma from giving birth)?

- Is there a lack of vaginal lubrication? If so, has your arousal pattern changed? Are you experiencing reduced or low sexual desire? Are you and your spouse enjoying adequate foreplay?

- Are you struggling in your marriage more generally? Are you in conflict, recovering from an emotional upheaval such as an affair, a miscarriage, or more general marital discord?

Drawing together as an intimate team is important here. As with some of the other sexual disorders, small but significant changes are important. For example, it may be that after having a baby, a couple is having sex less frequently because they are tired. They quickly attempt intercourse without adequate foreplay and the woman experiences sexual pain. She becomes anxious as a result and tenses up next time they attempt to have sex. She finds it difficult to get aroused, and so sex is less enjoyable, and a negative cycle is established. Even a case of untreated thrush, passed from the wife to her husband, can lead to dyspareunia if it is not tackled.

How is dyspareunia diagnosed?

Dyspareunia can be caused by a number of different conditions and it is therefore really important that you see your GP, ideally as a couple. Your doctor is likely to ask you about your pain, your lifestyle, and any other relevant medical and emotional issues. They will need to examine you, to see if you have any obvious physical cause for the pain. See Chapter 5 for details of a physical examination. If your GP is not confident in diagnosing or treating you, or they think you require more specific tests, they may refer you to a gynaecologist or another hospital specialist.

Self-help strategies

Vaginal lubricants

Vaginal lubricants can be bought from pharmacies or online without a prescription. A wide variety are available, either as water-based, silicone-based, mineral oil-based, or plant oil-based products, and are applied to the vagina and vulva (and the partner's penis if required) prior to sex. They act rapidly to provide short-term relief from vaginal dryness and related pain during sex, and are especially beneficial for women whose vaginal dryness, only or mainly, occurs during sex. Some lubricants are available on NHS prescription: ask your GP. If you experience pain or discomfort, I recommend a chemical-free lubricant, such as an organic lubricant, to minimise the risk of inflammation or further irritation. Avoid lubricants marketed as enhancing sensations, through heat or tingling, if the vulva or vagina is sensitive. If using condoms, avoid oil-based lubricants as they can damage the latex of the condom. See Appendix 3 for more information.

Vaginal moisturisers

Vaginal moisturisers are designed to rehydrate the dry mucosal tissue that lines the vaginal wall. These are absorbed and stick to the vaginal lining, mimicking natural vaginal secretions. They need to be applied regularly, from every day to once every two to three days. The more severe your symptoms, the more often you will need to use them, and they are effective for longer than lubricants. They work by maintaining vaginal moisture and acidity. Your GP can tell you more. Some vaginal moisturisers can be bought over the counter: hormone-based vaginal products are a medication and require a prescription.

Adequate foreplay

As well as using a vaginal lubricant, couples should engage in adequate foreplay to ensure the woman is sufficiently sexually aroused for penetrative sex. I would say that in the majority of women with dyspareunia, lack of sufficient foreplay to enable the woman to be adequately aroused is a significant causative factor. Ensuring that there is adequate foreplay will reduce the likelihood of sex being painful and increases sexual pleasure. Chapter 3 discusses expanding your sexual repertoire and increasing sexual arousal – a vibrator is often really helpful for this. Vibrators should be used with vaginal lubricants, especially if they are being inserted into the vagina. Ensure you have a compatible lubricant depending on the external material of the vibrator. See Appendix 3 for more on vibrators and lubricants.

Sexual positions

Positions chosen for sexual intercourse can affect the pain felt by women, and couples should discuss this. It may be better for the woman to go on top, so she has more control over the speed and depth of vaginal penetration. All attempts at penetration, whatever the sexual position, must be done after adequate vaginal lubrication has been applied, to the vagina, vulva, and the man's penis, and after adequate foreplay.

Vaginal dilators/vibrators

As we saw in Chapter 7, vaginal dilators are cone-shaped devices, graduated in size and designed to be gently and gradually inserted into the vagina. They are typically used by women experiencing vaginismus. They can also be used in dyspareunia, even in the absence of vaginismus, to help women gain confidence in their ability to accommodate vaginal penetration without pain. There are a number of vaginal dilator kits available on the market. Some women do not like using them and prefer different-sized vibrators. These can feel less clinical and can also be used to increase sexual arousal. Appendix 3 has more information.

Medical treatments

Sex and the menopause

Sex can become less enjoyable for many women during or after the menopause for many reasons. Vaginal dryness is prevalent among women of all ages, but is particularly common during and after the menopause, experienced by around 15 percent of premenopausal and up to 57 percent of postmenopausal women.[2] Vaginal or vulvovaginal atrophy (stiffening) also leads to dryness. These symptoms are also very likely to be experienced by women being treated for cancer who experience a surgical, radiotherapy or drug-induced menopause. During the reproductive years, oestrogen helps maintain the normal vaginal environment. As oestrogen levels fall during the menopause, the walls of the vagina become thinner and less pliable, often leading to inflammation and decreased vaginal lubrication. Some women also find their sexual desire declines, perhaps because of pain or emotional factors. Sexual pain can be managed medically but couples may need an integrated approach, combining symptom alleviation as well as psychosexual therapy.

Hormone treatment for women

If reduced levels of oestrogen and/or testosterone are largely responsible for sexual pain, you may benefit from hormone replacement therapy

(HRT). Oestrogen replacement can be given either systemically to increase levels throughout the whole body, or vaginally to increase levels in the genital area only. Systemic oestrogen can be given by tablet, patch or skin gel. It can improve sexual desire and reduce hot flushes, vaginal dryness, and low mood. Vaginal oestrogens are inserted into the vagina and come in a pessary, ring or cream. Long-term treatment is needed, because symptoms will return if the treatment is stopped. Your GP can discuss both the benefits and the risks of HRT with you.

Managing skin conditions

If you have eczema as a result of an allergy or irritation (contact dermatitis), you and your doctor will need to identify what may be causing it. Treatment usually involves topical steroid creams/ointments, and antihistamines can be used to relieve the inflammation and itching.

Self-help tips to promote vaginal health

- Avoid washing the vulval area with perfumed soap, bath oils, and shower gels: they can aggravate skin conditions and cause dryness. Instead, use lukewarm water alone or with a soap-free cleanser. Ask your GP or pharmacist for advice

- If you have a sensitive skin condition such as eczema or Lichen sclerosis, washing powder or liquid designed for sensitive skin is available for your laundry

- Avoid using intimate feminine wipes or any type of vaginal deodorant

- Wear underwear made solely from natural fibres, such as cotton or silk

- Use a vaginal lubricant every time you engage in sexual activity

If you have an allergy to, or are irritated by latex, plastic or spermicide, you should be able to get condoms that are less likely to cause a reaction. Ask your pharmacist for advice on this. If you are allergic to latex or spermicide, you will not be able to use a contraceptive diaphragm, as these are made of latex and should be used with a spermicide.

Vaginal thrush

Vaginal thrush is a common yeast infection that affects most women at some point in their lives and symptoms can be uncomfortable or painful.

Typical symptoms of vaginal thrush include:

- itching and soreness around the entrance of the vagina and the labia

- vaginal discharge – this is usually odourless and may be thick and white or thin and watery

- pain during sex

- a stinging sensation when passing urine

Thrush may be passed on through sexual contact or may develop for other reasons (e.g. during pregnancy, from taking antibiotics, or using products that irritate the vagina, or in women who have not had sex before or who have sex after a long period of abstinence). Antifungal treatment for thrush can be taken orally as a tablet, applied as a cream or used vaginally as a pessary. These products are available on prescription or over the counter at a pharmacy. Your spouse may also have thrush, and you may be passing it back and forth during sexual intercourse without being aware: not everyone experiences symptoms when they have thrush. If so, you will both need to be treated to avoid cross-infection. Talk to your GP as a couple.

Bacterial vaginosis (BV)

Bacterial vaginosis (BV) is a vaginal condition that can produce vaginal discharge and results from an overgrowth of certain types of bacteria in the vagina (it is commonly associated with Gardnerella Vaginalis bacteria). When these bacteria, which normally live in the vagina, become unbalanced, a woman may experience symptoms.

What causes this to happen is not fully known, but you are more likely to get it if you have an inter-uterine device (IUD: it is a contraception device), you use perfumed products in or around your vagina or simply when the acidity of your vagina changes slightly, for example when you have your period.

Symptoms include:

- an abnormal amount of vaginal discharge
- the vaginal discharge is thin and can be grey/white
- vaginal odour (foul-smelling or unpleasant fishy odour)
- vaginal discharge and odour that are often more noticeable after sexual intercourse
- pain with sexual intercourse or urination (these are rare symptoms)

BV can be a debilitating condition for a woman. Many women feel self-conscious because the symptoms, especially the associated vaginal odour, can be unpleasant. Some women repeatedly wash the vulval area to try to eliminate this but this can make the BV worse, which sets up a cycle that can be difficult to break. (See the self-help tips for promoting vaginal health on page 153).

Bacterial vaginosis is usually treated with antibiotic tablets or gel. These are prescribed by your GP or sexual health clinic. It's common for BV to come back, usually within three months of diagnosis. If this is the case, you will need re-treating. BV is not classed as a sexually transmitted infection (STI); however, it can be triggered by sex. Partners do not need treatment. If you develop BV in pregnancy, there's a small risk of complications, although these are rare.

You can buy treatments for BV without a prescription, such as lactic acid vaginal gel. I would always advise a patient to see their GP or Genito-Urinary Medicine (GUM) clinic, to have a proper swab test taken. This will diagnose if you have BV and then you can discuss appropriate treatment with the clinician.

Sexually transmitted infections (STIs)

Sexually transmitted infections (STIs) can be a sensitive issue in marriage. Some Christian couples choose to wait until they are married to have sex and others do not. One partner may have an STI, such as herpes or genital warts, be fully aware of this when entering into a new relationship, and can discuss it with the new partner. But other people may not be aware or may not feel able to discuss the issue with their spouse.

Signs of an STI for a woman may include: a change in vaginal discharge (colour and odour), discomfort during sexual intercourse, and painful urination. For men, symptoms may include discharge from the end of the penis (urethra). This may be clear or may be a foul-smelling, green/yellow discharge. Men may notice pain on urination and more generally in the genital region.

Some individuals do not experience symptoms from their STI, and so only realise they have one when their partner starts to experience the symptoms. This presents challenges. Firstly, the couple need to get fully screened for an STI to ensure they are both treated with appropriate medication, and they need to know how to manage the symptoms in future. The specialist treating them would discuss their treatment management. Some STIs, such as trichomoniasis, can be easily treated with antibiotics.

Discovering when the STI was contracted can cause emotional hurt in a relationship, particularly so if the partner who acquires the infection was not sexually active prior to marriage, but now is the only one suffering the symptoms. Couple counselling can help to manage both the physical and emotional effects of the STI.

If you think you have an STI, do not wait to see your GP, but visit your local GUM clinic. Often based in hospitals, these walk-in clinics enable people to be fully tested and treated for STIs. If you are a couple who are waiting until you are married to be sexually active but one partner has been sexually active historically and the other not, then I would encourage the partner who has been sexually active to be fully screened before the wedding. Therefore, any infections can be managed quickly, before you have sex with your spouse. If you have both been sexually active and have any concerns that you may have an STI or you want to know categorically that you do not have one, get tested. See Appendix 5 for more details.

Pelvic inflammatory disease (PID)

Pelvic inflammatory disease (PID) is a general term for infection of the upper genital tract, which includes the uterus (womb), fallopian tubes, and ovaries. The infection (which can be caused by chlamydia or gonorrhoea) is usually transmitted during sex, but PID is not always caused by sexually transmitted infections. If it is not treated early, PID may damage the fallopian tubes, which can increase the risk of ectopic pregnancy (where the pregnancy develops outside of the uterus) and infertility. Chlamydia and gonorrhoea are easily tested for and can be effectively treated with antibiotics. Treatment can be offered through your GP or GUM clinic.

Urinary tract infection (UTI)

A urinary tract infection (UTI), also known as cystitis, is an infection in the urine and can affect the bladder and the urethra (the tube that carries urine from the bladder to the urethral opening). UTIs are much more common in women than men. UTIs are not sexually transmitted but symptoms often develop after sex, usually in the first 36–48 hours. They can be very painful, especially in the bladder area and when urinating. They lead to the need to urinate frequently, blood in the urine, strong-smelling or dark urine, and fever. Your GP can test your urine to detect a UTI, which may clear up on its own or may require antibiotics.

If you suffer from frequent UTIs, there are a number of well-recognised self-help tips:

- Drink plenty of fluids to help flush harmful bacteria out of the bladder and urinary tract: good advice whether or not you have an infection. Take more fluid if you think you have one, and as a preventative measure for 48 hours after sexual intercourse

- Personal hygiene is important to minimise bacteria around the vagina and vulval area

- After opening your bowels, always wipe from front to back to avoid spreading bacteria over the vulva or urethra

- Avoid bubble baths, talcum powder, vaginal deodorants, and intimate feminine wipes

- Urinate immediately after having sex

- Use lots of vaginal lubrication to minimise trauma to the vagina and urethral area during intercourse

Your GP may refer you to an urologist for further investigations. Some urologists advocate taking one antibiotic tablet directly after sex, which can help stop infections. There are also some products that can be bought over the counter in pharmacies without a prescription that some women find helpful.

Vulvodynia

Vulvodynia refers to pain or soreness in the vulval area, not attributable to an infection. It usually involves a burning sensation and is caused by extreme sensitivity in the nerve fibres in the vulval area. Information about the Vulval Pain Society can be found in Appendix 5.

Symptoms

There are two types of vulvodynia:

- Unprovoked vulvodynia refers to when the pain occurs spontaneously (i.e. is not caused by pressure or local contact) and affects any part of the vulva.

- Provoked vulvodynia (also known as vestibulodynia) commonly occurs around the entrance to the vagina (vestibule), where the pain is caused by sexual or non-sexual touch (by sexual intercourse, inserting tampons, tight clothing, cycling etc.). Any form of vaginal penetration can be painful.

Vulvodynia is a condition with no known cause. For a small minority of women with vulvodynia, back problems can cause spinal nerve compression and referred pain in the vulval area.

A specific group of tricyclic antidepressant tablets are a standard treatment for vulvodynia, because they have a specific impact on nerve endings and as a result can reduce pain. Gabapentin or Pregabalin are also used to treat nerve pain such as vulvodynia. The treatment is in tablet form, starting at a low dose and then increasing every few days until the pain subsides. The response to treatment may take several weeks, and treatment may be necessary for three to six months. You would need to discuss this with your GP who may recommend combining drug therapy with sex therapy to reduce pain during intercourse. This can be very effective.

Endometriosis

Endometriosis is a condition in which cells like those lining the uterus grow elsewhere in the body. These cells behave in the same way as those in the uterus and follow the menstrual cycle, so each month they build up, break down, then bleed. However, while the blood of a period can leave the uterus through the vagina, it can't leave from anywhere else in the body. This is a long-term, debilitating condition which causes painful and often heavy periods. It may also lead to tiredness, depression, sexual problems, and infertility. It usually affects women of child-bearing years.

If your GP thinks you may have endometriosis, you will probably be referred to a gynaecologist for further tests. The results will determine if you need medical or surgical treatment.

Female genital mutilation (FGM)

You may have heard about female genital mutilation (FGM) in the media. It is a ritual practice where the female genitals are deliberately cut, injured or changed, and is usually carried out on girls between infancy and the age of fifteen, normally before puberty starts. It is illegal in the UK and is considered a form of child abuse. FGM can seriously harm health and well-being, causing long-term problems with sex, childbirth, and mental health. It can result in reduced sexual desire and a lack of pleasurable sensations.

Your GP can help if you have been affected by FGM, and refer you to a specialist – a gynaecologist and/or a sex therapist. See Appendix 5 for further support.

Persistent genital arousal disorder

Persistent genital arousal disorder (PGAD) is a newly recognised condition, where the woman (or rarely, the man) complains of long periods of genital arousal that come on spontaneously and are unwanted. They are not associated with preceding sexual desire and are highly distressing. It may be associated with a feeling described by some patients as "restlessness", and many sufferers masturbate and orgasm repeatedly to get rid of the symptoms, usually unsuccessfully.

Below are the features of PGAD that are necessary for diagnosis:[3,4,5]

🖉 The symptoms are characteristic of sexual arousal (genital fullness/ swelling and sensitivity with or without nipple fullness/swelling) or dysesthesia (an abnormal unpleasant sensation felt when touched, caused by damage to peripheral nerves), which persist for an extended period of time (hours or days) and do not subside completely on their own

🖉 Symptoms of genital arousal do not resolve when the woman has an orgasm. She may find that she requires repeated orgasms over hours or days for the symptoms to stop

🖉 Symptoms of arousal are unrelated to any sense of sexual excitement or desire

🖉 Persistent sexual arousal may be triggered not only by a sexual activity but also by a seemingly non-sexual stimulus or by no apparent stimulus at all

🖉 Symptoms are experienced as intrusive and unwanted

🖉 The symptoms cause the woman, at least, a moderate degree of distress

PGAD needs to be differentiated from hypersexuality, which can be defined as "frequently repetitive sexual urges, fantasies or behaviours".[6] Repetitive sexual behaviour such as masturbation may be a clinical feature of both PGAD and hypersexuality. However, in PGAD, masturbation is only undertaken because of unwanted genital arousal or dysesthesia. PGAD is a rare condition (I have only potentially seen one case in clinical practice) and requires specialist assessment by a multidisciplinary team, including a physician or gynaecologist, sex therapist, and a physiotherapist. If you suspect you have PGAD then you will need to see your GP who will then refer you to a gynaecologist for further investigation.

Sexual pain in men

Sexual pain in men is rare but it does exist. The usual causes for this are:

- tight frenulum: where the band of skin between the foreskin and glans penis is tight. This can tear, causing bleeding, scarring, and pain

- tight foreskin (phimosis): the foreskin is too tight to be pulled back over the head of the penis (glans). This can sometimes cause pain when the penis is erect and, in rare cases, passing urine may be difficult

- recurrent balanitis: the foreskin and head of the penis become inflamed and infected

- paraphimosis: the foreskin cannot be returned to its original position after being pulled back, causing the head of the penis to become swollen and painful. In this case, only immediate treatment to replace the foreskin will prevent serious complications, such as restricted blood flow to the penis

These conditions are often resolved by circumcision and non-surgical options such as topical steroids. A tight frenulum is treated by frenuloplasty, a very simple operation to lengthen the frenulum. This can often be carried out under local anaesthetic. See your GP if you experience pain when you get an erection, or at any other time during sexual intimacy. You may then be referred to an urologist for further assessment and treatment.

Conclusion

Sexual pain, though rarely discussed, is common, and can have a serious effect on how women and their partners view sex. The sufferer can easily fall into a negative cycle of thinking and can quickly avoid sex altogether. It takes courage and persistence to challenge this negative cycle and to work through strategies that can help.

There are lots of practical things that couples can implement when it comes to sexual pain and it is important to address the pain as soon as possible. Sex does not have to include penetration, and while the problems are being addressed, there are other ways to enjoy intimate contact (see Chapter 3). Keep talking to your spouse, explore what does work for you, and focus on these while seeking longer term solutions.

> *You will keep in perfect peace those whose minds are steadfast,*
> *because they trust in you. Trust in the LORD for ever, for the LORD,*
> *the LORD himself, is the Rock eternal.*
>
> *Isaiah 26:3–4*

References

1. Mitchell, K., Geary, R., et al. (2017) Painful sex (dyspareunia) in women: prevalence and associated factors in a British population probability survey BJOG. *An International Journal of Obstetrics and Gynaecology*, 124 (11), 1689-1697.

2. Palacios, S. (2009) Managing urogenital atrophy. *Maturities*, 63, 315–18.

3. Leiblum, S. Nathan, S. (2001) Persistent sexual arousal syndrome: A newly discovered pattern of female sexuality. *Journal of Sex and Marital Therapy*, 27, 365-80.

4. Goldmeier, D., Leiblum, S. (2006) Persistent genital arousal disorder – a new syndrome entity. *International Journal of STD and AIDS*, 17, 215–16.

5. Waldinger, M., Schweitzer, D. (2009) Persistent genital arousal disorder in 18 Dutch women: Part II. A syndrome clustered with restless legs and overactive bladder. *Journal of Sexual Medicine*, 6(2), 482–97.

6. Kafka, M. (2010) Hypersexual disorder: a proposed diagnosis for DSM-V. *Archives of Sexual Behavior*, 39, 377–400.

CHAPTER NINE

Early Ejaculation

Love does not delight in evil but rejoices with the truth.
It always protects, always trusts, always hopes, always perseveres.

1 Corinthians 13:6-7

There are two main ejaculatory problems that can affect men: early ejaculation and delayed ejaculation.

Early ejaculation

The most common ejaculatory condition is early ejaculation (EE). This term has largely replaced the historically used term "premature ejaculation", and it is also referred to as rapid ejaculation. I will use the term early ejaculation. Delayed ejaculation and orgasmic disorders in men will be addressed in the next chapter.

According to the International Society of Sexual Medicine (ISSM), early ejaculation is associated with being unable to delay ejaculation when attempting vaginal penetration, and ejaculation almost always happening either before or within around one minute of vaginal penetration.[1] The results of this can be devastating, and often attempts at sexual intercourse will be avoided altogether, because of the performance anxiety.

Situational or absolute?

It is important to make the distinction between situational early ejaculation – early ejaculation that happens in certain situations, i.e. with a partner and not when the man masturbates alone – and absolute early ejaculation, when the early ejaculation happens regardless of the situation.

Primary or secondary?

It is also important to distinguish between lifelong (primary) and acquired (secondary) early ejaculation. The former means it has always been a difficulty, whereas the latter has occurred after a period of being able to ejaculate when desired.

EE is now considered to be the most common male sexual disorder. Research into this condition indicates that anywhere between 8 and 30 percent of men experience early ejaculation.[2,3] It is difficult to get accurate figures because some men report early ejaculation when it is only experienced occasionally, not consistently. Other research suggests rates are more likely to be about 8–10 percent of all sexually active men.

In Masters and Johnson's male sexual arousal cycle there are four distinct phases: arousal, plateau, orgasm, and resolution (see image on page 48).[4] Early ejaculation is considered a disorder of the orgasm phase of this response cycle. If a man cannot sustain an adequate period of time in the plateau phase, early ejaculation can occur. Most cases are caused by the man being unable to control the ejaculatory response. Sometimes he has not learnt to recognise or control the feeling just prior to the "point of ejaculatory inevitability" – the sensation that tells him he is about to orgasm. I often compare this sensation to that experienced just before we sneeze. The "pre-sneeze" can be easily missed.

What causes early ejaculation?

Early ejaculation is often considered to be the result of sexual inexperience and is thus more common in adolescents and young men.[5] EE is believed to have a number of different causes and can be treated successfully without the causes always becoming clear. The usual predisposing, precipitating, and maintaining factors that are considered for other sexual difficulties are assessed for early ejaculation.

Predisposing factors

Sometimes early ejaculation can be attributed to the individual man's biological predisposition, and that is not always easy to quantify. I have worked with a small number of patients presenting with EE and identified a common strand: all of them were often quite anxious – not just about the EE but more generally.

Neurological risk factors for EE include cerebral disease such as brain injury, Parkinson's disease, and epilepsy. Urological conditions such as prostatitis (inflammation of the prostate gland) can impact EE, as can withdrawal from certain substances, particularly opiate drugs (e.g. morphine). Relationship issues and past sexual history are also important. I would ask the standard questions relating to predisposing factors (see Part II – Introduction).

Some men have experienced early ejaculation from the very first sexual experience they have had and been taunted as a result, which has overshadowed new relationships. How the man learnt to masturbate is also very important. If, as a teenager, he got into a practice of masturbating very quickly, either through fear of getting caught or guilt, then this might store up problems for later, when he meets a partner.

Men often say they cannot talk to their friends about sexual difficulties, and macho banter about how long a man can "last" adds further pressure. Many men have not had adequate sex education and this can create unrealistic expectations, as can watching a lot of pornography. Men can think that they should be able to last indefinitely whilst having sex – not realising that pornography is edited and full of illusions. Most men cannot engage in foreplay and penetrative sex, for long periods, with multiple partners.

Precipitating (triggering) factors

Some drugs can impact ejaculatory function or arousal. Other factors include illness, surgery, or more emotional issues such as redundancy or bereavement. A man who has never had a sexual relationship prior to marriage may find the build-up to the wedding and a heightened sense of arousal can lead to early ejaculation. This in turn can lead to performance anxiety: every time he has sex, he worries he will ejaculate too quickly, and then he does.

Erection problems can also contribute to EE, as some men will ejaculate early if they think they might lose their erection. There is a pressure to finish before the erection goes. I have had a number of patients referred to me with EE but assessment reveals that erectile dysfunction is the real issue: successful treatment of the erectile dysfunction resolves both.

Maintaining factors

Maintaining factors might be psychological: marriage difficulties, different attitudes towards sexual intimacy, or different levels of desire. If a couple has waited till marriage to have sex, early ejaculation can be a huge disappointment, and if they do not talk about it, they can give up on sex altogether. I have worked with couples where the man always ejaculates prior to penetration through little or minimal stimulation and the couple are seeking treatment because they want to try to conceive. Some men can find that just thinking about something sexually stimulating can trigger ejaculation, without any direct penile stimulation. Again, this will be difficult if the couple want to conceive and the resulting pressure will make things worse. And if the woman also suffers from pain on intercourse, the man can try to hurry to relieve her pain.

However, what one couple might define as early ejaculation, another couple will not. If a couple enjoy penetrative sex, and this lasts less than one minute, and both partners are satisfied with this and it causes no distress, then we would not consider this to be early ejaculation.

Treatment for early ejaculation

Early ejaculation must be tackled by the intimate team. It is not the man's problem to sort out: it is for both of you.

What to do first

If you are struggling with early ejaculation, considering the material above, you may already have decided whether it is primary or secondary, situational or absolute. This may help as you think about possible causes. See your GP, even if you think the EE is situational, meaning more likely to be psychologically or relationally influenced. They will give you a physical examination and refer you to a specialist such as an urologist. Your GP may also want to do some blood tests to check your hormones and as part of a general men's health check.

If the GP is able to identify a cause such as prostatitis (inflammation of the prostate gland), they will be able to treat this, or refer you to an urologist for treatment. This may resolve the EE. Or it may be decided that erectile dysfunction is the main cause – and this will be treated.

Treatment of early ejaculation can be either behavioural treatment and/or drug treatment and I am going to discuss each of these briefly below.

Behavioural treatment

Behavioural treatment involves the man and his partner undertaking a self-help programme of simple exercises at home, the "stop/start" technique. The exercises enable the man to become aroused and then to stop the stimulation. They can be done by the man alone, or preferably with his partner. If you are single and want to gain more ejaculatory control, however, you can do the exercises on your own.

The stop/start technique

In Chapter 2, I have set out some exercises that encourage men to familiarise themselves with their genital area, to become comfortable touching themselves and increasingly aware of the different sensations this can create. Doing these can help men to recognise the feeling just before the sensation that they are going to ejaculate, the "pre-sneeze" sensation.

Step 1: While having a bath or shower, touch your penis and scrotal area, in an intentional way: the idea is to fully connect with what touching this area feels like. Men can get very used to stimulating their genitals in a very specific personalised way which can make it more challenging when a partner then touches them differently. Some men with situational EE experience a heightened sense of arousal when their partner touches their genitals. When a man touches himself he has full control over the touch, grip, and speed involved. Use your hand and the sensation of the water, to experiment with soft touching, light touching, slow touching. Engage in what you are experiencing: this will be an integral part of the exercise later, if you have a spouse. You may feel aroused and you can experiment with experiencing this sensation and then letting it pass. Repeat this exercise a couple of times, eventually allowing yourself to reach orgasm, the point of ejaculation. Try to practise this exercise every day or so for a week, before you move on to the next step.

Step 2: Choose a place where you will be comfortable and undisturbed. Gradually start stimulation of the penis (a lubricated hand helps). Stop just before you think you are about to reach the point of inevitability, where you know you will ejaculate if you continue stimulation.

Step 3: Rest, and stop all stimulation for thirty to sixty seconds, until the need to ejaculate subsides. Begin stimulating the penis again, stopping or reducing the stimulation when you become aware of the sensation just before point of inevitability.

Step 4: Repeat the above steps four or five times, until you begin to recognise when you are about to ejaculate. After repeating these exercises, then allow ejaculation to occur.

You will need to repeat these exercises for a couple of weeks. Do them in the presence of your spouse so that she feels included, having got used to doing them alone first. When you have built up confidence, ask your wife to stimulate you with her hand following the steps 1–4 as above, perhaps without a lubricated hand, as this can heighten the feelings of arousal. As you become more confident with gaining ejaculatory control, use lubrication.

The stop/start technique can then progress to the squeeze technique. This involves your partner stimulating you up to the point of inevitability, then firmly squeezing the penis where the glans (rounded top) joins the main shaft, using the thumb and forefinger. The sensation of being about to ejaculate will reduce. There may be some softening of your erection, until stimulation begins again. This technique can be a little more difficult to master.

For more information, I recommend two very good books, which have much more detail about this programme. *How to Overcome Premature Ejaculation* by Helen Singer Kaplan is quite an old book but it is simple, short, and very easy to follow.[6] It gives clear instructions for undertaking the stop/start programme and the squeeze technique and could be used by a couple or a single man. *Coping with Premature Ejaculation* by Michael Metz and Barry McCarthy is more comprehensive, a book specifically designed for couples.[7] It looks at a whole variety of impacting factors and gives clear advice about different treatment options, including the behavioural programmes using the stop/start technique. Metz and McCarthy also wrote *Enduring Desire*, with its emphasis on how to incorporate the principle of the intimate team to help manage the EE.[8] The book also covers pharmacological (drug) treatments. However, it was published in 2003 and is by American authors. The drug treatments we now use for EE in the UK have changed, so I will discuss additional drug treatments below.

Condoms

Using condoms, including those with anaesthetic cream, can reduce the sensation of heightened arousal and increase time to ejaculation. Ask your pharmacist about what they stock. Alternatively, these can be ordered online. However, for some couples this will be a short-term solution, particularly if they want to conceive.

Drug treatments

Over the last five years there have been some advances in the management of EE and the treatment options now available, including a new topical (spray) treatment licensed for use in the UK. As a sex therapist, I see patients with EE who have tried drug treatments but have either not tolerated their side effects or found them ineffective. For these men their EE is more complex and they want to explore the impacts of other relationship and psychological factors. Nor do all men want to be reliant on drugs for the longer term, as EE often returns if treatment is stopped. With psychological erection difficulties, it is often worth taking a dual approach. Medication can give a helpful initial confidence boost, but working with a therapist, a longer-term solution can be found, looking at relationship, emotional or psychological factors. These may be more complex and require more time to address.

Antidepressants

For many years a specific group of antidepressant drugs have been used to treat EE: selective serotonin reuptake inhibitors (SSRIs). The side effect of these drugs is to delay ejaculation. SSRIs used for this purpose include Paroxetine, Sertraline, and Fluoxetine. Some men experience an immediate improvement; others have to take the medication for a few weeks before they see the full effects. Other side effects of SSRIs are usually mild and should improve after two to three weeks. They can include fatigue, feeling and being sick, diarrhoea, and excessive sweating.

Dapoxetine

Dapoxetine (Priligy) is an SSRI licensed in the UK in 2013. It acts much faster than the above SSRIs and can be used "on demand" when needed, as opposed to being taken daily. Initially 30mg is taken one to three hours before sexual activity. If the response is inadequate, and the man has had no adverse reactions or symptoms such as fainting, the dose can be increased to 60mg as needed. You will usually be advised to take it between one and three hours before sex, but not more than once a day. Your response to treatment will then be reviewed after four weeks (or six doses), and again every six months.

Dapoxetine is not suitable for all men diagnosed with EE, including those with heart, kidney or liver problems, or men over the age of 65 years. It can also interact with other medications such as other antidepressants and some heart medication. Alcohol should also be avoided when taking Dapoxetine and this can make it an unappealing option for some men. Common side effects can include headaches, dizziness, and nausea.

Any man/couple interested in trying Dapoxetine or an SSRI must be seen by their GP or hospital specialist so the risks and benefits can be assessed and all treatment options explored.

Fortacin

Fortacin is a topical spray that has recently been licensed for use in the UK. I have no experience of using this new treatment with my patients but the spray acts as a local anaesthetic to the glans of the penis (the most sensitive part) to desensitise the area and reduce feelings of heightened arousal. The recommended dose is three sprays applied to cover the glans penis. A maximum of three doses can be used within 24 hours with at least four hours between doses.

Before considering this medication, it is important that you both seek advice from your GP, to get all the adequate information to ensure you are using it safely. Fortacin can be transferred to your spouse and cause transitory vaginal numbness. If you do want to use it, the advice is to wash the glans penis as thoroughly as possible five minutes after applying the spray, but prior to intercourse. At present, Fortacin is only available on a private prescription.

Conclusion

Early ejaculation, though it can be defined medically, is a much more subjective disorder than erectile dysfunction. Couples' sexual styles vary enormously. Some enjoy penetrative intercourse that lasts a long time: others focus much more on foreplay. So EE and whether it is a problem can only be defined by the couple, as we have seen. What causes one couple distress will be considered a normal part of love-making for another.

Unlike erection problems, where couples are usually in agreement about how this difficulty impacts sexual intimacy, you and your partner may have very different views about whether there is a problem with early ejaculation. So you need to talk to each other. Are you both satisfied? If one of you perceives there is a problem but the other does not, what is causing this discrepancy? Sometimes when something is subjective it can make the discussion more challenging. It might mean that the woman feels that her husband is ejaculating earlier than she would like but he doesn't realise this. Or the man may have unrealistic ideas about how long he should be able to last before he ejaculates, and this is placing unwanted pressure on one or both partners.

Draw together as an intimate team in an open-minded way. Listen as well as talk, and be gentle with each other, so as not to damage confidence or create a sense of shame. These discussions are not easy but they are possible, and a sex therapist might help pave the way to a deeper level of communication, and greater sexual intimacy and pleasure.

> *Be completely humble and gentle; be patient,*
> *bearing with one another in love.*
>
> *Ephesians 4:2*

References

1. www.issm.info/news/sex-health-headlines/definition-of-premature-ejaculation-pe

2. E. Serefoglu, "Epidemiology of early ejaculation" in E.A. Jannini, C.G. McMahon and M.D. Waldinger, (Eds), *Early ejaculation: From etiology to diagnosis and treatment*, (New York: Springer, 2013), pp. 45–52.

3. Jannini, E., Lenzi, A. (2005) Epidemiology of early ejaculation. *Current Opinion in Urology*, 15(6), 399–403.

4. W.H. Masters, V.E. Johnson, *Human Sexual Response*, (New York: Bantam Books, 1966).

5. Jern, P., Santtila, P., et al. (2009) Evidence for a genetic etiology to ejaculatory dysfunction: genetic effects on ejaculatory dysfunction. *International Journal of Impotence Research*, 21, 62–67.

6. Helen Singer Kaplan, *How to Overcome Premature Ejaculation*, (London: Routledge, 1989).

7. Michael E. Metz and Barry W. McCarthy, *Coping with Premature Ejaculation*, (Oakland: New Harbinger, 2004).

8. Michael E. Metz and Barry W. McCarthy, *Enduring Desire: Your Guide to Lifelong Intimacy*, (London: Routledge, 2010).

CHAPTER TEN

Delayed Ejaculation and Orgasmic Disorders in Men

Cast all your anxiety on him
because he cares for you.

1 Peter 5:7

Early ejaculation, as we have seen, is the most commonly experienced ejaculatory problem in men. Other ejaculatory and orgasmic difficulties include:

- delayed ejaculation

- retrograde ejaculation

- anorgasmia

Delayed ejaculation (DE) is the delay or inability to achieve ejaculation despite the presence of adequate sexual stimulation and the desire to ejaculate. There are a number of factors that help a diagnosis of DE to be made. It needs to:

🌿 be experienced during almost all occasions of partnered or solo sexual activity

🌿 cause distress for the man and not be within his control. It is also well recognised that DE can have significant negative consequences for the partner and the relationship as a whole, especially if the couple are trying to conceive

Primary or secondary?

As with early ejaculation, it is important to ascertain whether the condition is lifelong (primary) or acquired (secondary). Lifelong delayed ejaculation is very rare. Delayed ejaculation is usually experienced after a period of normal functioning.

Situational or absolute?

It is also important to establish whether the delayed ejaculation is situational (present with a partner for example, but not when the man stimulates himself sexually), or absolute (the same regardless of the circumstances). About 25 percent of men present with absolute DE.[1]

What causes delayed ejaculation?

There are virtually no research studies on delayed ejaculation and it therefore remains one of the more complex sexual disorders to treat, partly because we don't really understand the condition, making it the least common and least understood of the male sexual difficulties. A study looking at DE showed that it occurred in less than 1 percent of men.[1]

We do know that sexual desire and arousal originate in the brain and central nervous system, and the process of orgasm is a highly individual one, influenced by a host of physical and emotional factors. Before discussing assessment and treatment options for DE, I want to mention two other ejaculatory disorders.

Retrograde ejaculation

Retrograde ejaculation is an uncommon condition that occurs when semen is expelled into the bladder instead of going out through the urethra during ejaculation. It is mainly caused by the bladder neck not closing, which forces semen backwards into the bladder rather than forward out of the penis. It may be caused by neurological problems due to diabetes or multiple sclerosis, spinal cord injury, and some prescription medications (mainly for blood pressure control). It is also fairly common after some types of prostate surgery. Men tend to notice that there is little ejaculate on orgasm and when they pass urine after they have ejaculated, it can appear cloudy. The sensation of ejaculation may also be reduced.

There is no treatment for retrograde ejaculation, and although it is not harmful, some men and their partners find this change in function difficult. It can take a period of psychological adjustment for both parties, and sex therapy can be helpful through this process of reframing sexual expectations. In theory this condition could also impact fertility, although I have never seen this in practice. This is probably because the conditions or surgery that might cause retrograde ejaculation are more likely in older men.

Anorgasmia and anejaculation

Anorgasmia is an inability to reach orgasm even after sexual stimulation and excitement. A man will be able to get and maintain a good erection but despite feeling sexually aroused, he will be unable to orgasm. Orgasm is usually associated with ejaculation, but in fact men can experience the pleasurable feeling of an orgasm without ejaculating, and this is called anejaculation. This is a relatively uncommon condition but can be evident in men who have had their prostate gland removed (the organ that produces most of the seminal fluid). There is no treatment for anejaculation, but some couples find sex therapy helpful in adjusting to this change.

Assessment of delayed ejaculation and anorgasmia

With any of the ejaculatory and orgasmic disorders outlined above, the clinician and patient/couple need to be thinking about predisposing, precipitating, and maintaining factors. Many of the questions around early ejaculation are relevant to delayed ejaculation and anorgasmia. These questions consider physical as well as emotional and relationship factors.

Predisposing factors

Primary delayed ejaculation/anorgasmia is rare and so most men will have had a period of enjoying normal ejaculatory function and orgasm. For this reason, predisposing factors tend to be less relevant than precipitating or maintaining factors.

Precipitating (triggering) factors

These are things that happen in the run-up to, or immediately prior to, the experience of delayed ejaculation/anorgasmia. These could be physical, such as starting on a medication which impacts ejaculatory function or arousal, such as antidepressants or drugs to treat high blood pressure. Other medical factors such as diabetes, or surgery that interferes with the brain or nerve supply to the pelvis and genital region, can also impact ejaculatory function. There could be emotional factors such as redundancy or bereavement. Relationship factors are also important. If a couple are trying to conceive, the underlying pressure can make the man unable to relax and enjoy the sexual intimacy. If the man worries about not ejaculating, he may find it hard to reach orgasm. This is another form of performance anxiety, a common theme in almost all sexual problems. The more one worries about the problem, the more difficult it becomes to fully engage in the moment with one's spouse and so the problem is perpetuated.

Maintaining factors

If the delayed ejaculation or anorgasmia is situational I would be interested in understanding how the man experiences different types of sexual stimulation. For example, some men can more easily ejaculate and orgasm when they masturbate or when their partner gives them oral sex, but this is more difficult with vaginal penetration. Some men may have a very specific masturbation technique that cannot readily be replicated during vaginal penetration. This might be due to the intensity of sexual stimulation when engaging in these different sexual acts. Sometimes I have worked with men who did not really want to have children, and this has impacted their ability to ejaculate in vaginal penetration. This is the opposite of the man I described above, whose desire to conceive with his wife is so intense that it is adversely affecting his ability to ejaculate, despite wanting to.

The relationship dynamic between the couple can also have an influence on arousal and ejaculation. Has the intensity of the sexual intimacy changed? Has there been an affair or marital tension? Are there reasons why it is harder for one or other partner or the couple as a whole to fully engage, both physically and emotionally, in sex?

In Chapter 2 I talk about the importance of fully inhabiting our bodies; this is particularly important when we are engaging in sexual intimacy. Perhaps there is a reason why this has become challenging.

Treatment for delayed ejaculation and anorgasmia

If you are experiencing delayed ejaculation or anorgasmia which is causing you distress, it is advisable to see your GP. Both conditions are relatively rare, and so your GP may want to refer you to a hospital specialist, usually a urologist. They will almost certainly do a physical examination, including checking your prostate gland, and may do some blood tests to see if the hormone levels are within normal range.

Depending on the test results, you may then be referred to a sex and relationship therapist, who may help you find ways to increase sexual arousal and stimulation. This may improve the delayed ejaculation or anorgasmia. Time to ejaculation may not change, nor the ability to orgasm, but you may develop strategies to reduce the distress this causes you and your partner.

No drug treatment exists for either condition, and so the focus is on management. This might include considering whether a new medication has triggered the issue. Perhaps the medication can be altered or stopped, to see if that helps. Couples can also work together to find ways of intensifying sexual stimulation, perhaps having more foreplay. As men get older, they often need more "hands on" stimulation of the penis and scrotal area to get and stay aroused. This might include oral sex or the woman manually stimulating her husband's penis, reducing the time to orgasm and ejaculation. Just as many women find using a vibrator enhances pleasure, men can also find this to be the case. The man can use the vibrator on the shaft of the penis or around the scrotal area, or use a vibrating penis ring to increase the intensity of pleasure. He might then try vaginal penetration, then stop and stimulate himself with his hand, to achieve orgasm. This can be helpful because he can control the speed and intensity needed to reach orgasm.

Delayed ejaculation and anorgasmia can be a challenge to treat and highlight the need for the couple to work together as an intimate team. Clear uninhibited communication will allow them to find ways of enhancing their sexual experience, and to work together to achieve that. Some couples struggle when the therapist cannot guarantee the situation will improve, but using the suggestions above can help. Success will depend on the couple's ability to remain emotionally close and intimate, whilst meeting both partners' sexual expectations. Sometimes this means trying new things or adapting one's expectations.

Some couples feel sad when they are unable to enjoy sexual intimacy in the way they once did, and therapy can help them grieve for their loss and adjust their expectations about sex. In my experience, couples who are able to approach love-making in a creative way, focusing on the process rather than the performance, are often able to continue to enjoy sexual intimacy that is mutually satisfying, despite the challenges they have had to address.

References

1. Althof, S. (2012) Psychological interventions for delayed ejaculation/ orgasm. *International Journal of Impotence Research*, 24, 131–36.

CHAPTER ELEVEN

Low Sexual Desire/Arousal

With my body I honour you, all that I am I give to you,
and all that I have I share with you, within the love
of God, Father, Son and Holy Spirit.

Church of England marriage service

What are sexual desire and sexual arousal?

Sexual desire is the interest we have in sexual activity, including sexual thoughts, fantasies or actual sexual contact with ourselves or another person, and this process usually starts in our minds. Sex drive or libido is the biological driving force for us to act on our desire and pursue sexual activity. Although the basis for sexual drive is a biological force, it is a complex process incorporating many factors such as our hormones, general health and fitness, self-esteem, past sexual experiences, confidence, and the quality of our relationship (if we are in one), to name just a few.

In this chapter I am going to outline a number of disorders that are medically classified as separate disorders, but the similar way in which they are assessed and managed means that it makes sense to categorise them under the broader heading of sexual desire and arousal.

Definitions for hypo (low) sexual desire disorder have separate diagnostic criteria for men and women.

Hypoactive sexual desire disorder (HSDD)

Men who have little or no desire for sex may be diagnosed with hypoactive sexual desire disorder, or HSDD. The following four conditions must be met for a diagnosis of HSDD to be made:

1. Deficient or absent sexual thoughts or fantasies

2. Deficient or absent desire for sexual activity

3. Low desire must be of six months' duration or longer

4. Must cause clinically significant distress

The severity of HSDD is classified not by the deficiency of sexual desire but by the level of distress this creates for the man. What might constitute HSDD in one man, who is distressed by it, would not in another who was not. If the lack of sexual intimacy is acceptable to both partners, it would not be considered a problem.

Female sexual interest/arousal disorder

Female sexual interest/arousal disorder (FSIAD) is the medical term for low desire and sexual interest in women. For a diagnosis of FSIAD to be made, a clinician would be looking for:

- absent or reduced interest in sexual activity

- absent or reduced sexual or erotic thoughts or fantasies

🌿 absent or reduced initiation of sexual activity and typically being non-responsive to the partner's attempts to initiate sexual activity

🌿 absent or reduced sexual excitement or pleasure during sexual activity

For a diagnosis to be made in either a man or a woman, a clinician would be looking to ascertain that the symptoms had persisted for at least six months and cause significant distress to the individual.

The clinician would also be looking to determine that the symptoms were not caused by problems such as:

🌿 another mental health disorder such as depression

🌿 severe relationship problems, leading to distress

🌿 the presence of other major life stresses

🌿 medication side effects, substance abuse, or medical conditions which have the potential to affect desire/arousal

Whilst I think it is important to give the reader the correct medical name for the various disorders, as these names may be used if you are seen by a specialist, for the purposes of this chapter I will use the simpler term "low desire" to describe low sexual desire disorders for both men and women.

Diagnosis for low desire/arousal disorder

Predisposing factors

Individuals and couples vary so much in how they think about sex and experience desire. It is impossible to present every possible scenario. Assessing a patient or couple involves accumulating lots of pieces of information, like collecting pieces of an intricate jigsaw puzzle. When I am completing an assessment, I consider with the patient (or ideally the couple) a number of different "jigsaw pieces" – biological, relationship, social, and sexual enjoyment factors.

Biological factors

There are many biological factors that impact the way our bodies function and respond, and I ask lots of detailed questions. These include:

- hormone deficiency, including low oestrogen or testosterone, menopausal changes, infertility

- medication – this might include antidepressants or anxiety drugs, or drugs used to treat cardiac conditions or high blood pressure

- medical conditions – diabetes, high blood pressure, disease of the arteries (atherosclerosis), thyroid problems, or Parkinson's disease

- treatment for cancer, including surgery, radiotherapy or chemotherapy

- sexually transmitted infections

- sexual dysfunction – it is not uncommon for a patient to be referred to me with "low libido" and the problem is actually erectile dysfunction or dyspareunia

Arousal issues

For us to want to engage in sex, we need to enjoy it or at least believe there is hope we might enjoy it. It makes complete sense that if sex is not enjoyable, disappointing or boring we are not going to feel aroused, and we are not going to be sending messages to our brain that this is a good activity which we regularly want to repeat. We are more likely to be reinforcing a message that sex is not enjoyable, and we want to find ways to avoid it.

When I am assessing arousal issues, I would ask the following questions.

🍃 Are both parties able to get fully sexually aroused with their partner; if not, what is preventing arousal in one or both?

Some patients tell me that they have low sexual desire. On further questioning, I discover they do have desire, but the lack of reciprocal desire or responsiveness from their partner is a turn-off. This makes it difficult for them to remain aroused. The issue here is not so much the presenting person but the dynamic with their partner, and possibly lack of desire in them. I always encourage couples to seek help together, because this subtle piece of information can give us a lot of useful clues to what is happening.

🍃 Is sex usually pleasurable when the couple attempts it? Does the spouse with low desire still have sexual thoughts and fantasies, and do they ever sexually stimulate themselves or masturbate?

This is a crucial question because it can give us a big clue as to what some of the underlying issues might be. If the person does not have sexual fantasies, thoughts or masturbate, we would describe the lack of desire as absolute. However, if the person does have sexual thoughts, etc., this suggests the lack of desire is situational. Perhaps the man says he is able to get fully aroused when masturbating but has little or no desire to engage in sexual intimacy with his wife. Similarly, a wife might have erotic thoughts and get physically aroused watching pornography, but she has no feeling of sexual desire or arousal when her husband initiates sex. This information can be crucial in helping us establish whether there is a relational aspect to the lack of desire.

🍃 Why has the focus of desire moved from the partner? If we assume that their spouse was at one time the object of their sexual desire, what has changed?

For some couples it can be difficult to adjust to the changing perceptions of themselves or their partner that everyday life can cause, and sometimes this can bring up painful issues. Perhaps the arrival of children has reframed how we view our partner sexually. For some couples it can be quite difficult for both to adjust to things like breastfeeding. It can change the way a woman views her breasts, or a man views his partner's breasts. A change in role can also have an impact. For instance, if one spouse has acted as a carer to their partner for a period of time, this could then mean they have viewed their spouse as a patient.

Perhaps there has been a change in social circumstances through unemployment or retirement which has had an impact on how the individual has traditionally viewed themselves in the family unit. This can affect how they see their masculinity or femininity. If a woman is used to her husband being the main breadwinner and this role reverses, this can challenge how we perceive traditionally held female or male roles and this can impact how we might view our spouse.

Perhaps one partner has gained weight and this is affecting how they view themselves or how their spouse views them. They may have become self-conscious about exposing their body, because of a change in the way their body looks as a result of surgery, a mastectomy, or colostomy. The spouse gets dressed and undressed in another room, and gradually over time there is a diminishing of sexual contact or physical intimacy. All these factors can impact how we feel about ourselves and also our partner sexually.

Painful though these issues can be, it is important that honesty is the starting point in moving forward and addressing problems, and seeking professional help can be a good starting place for this. As a therapist, I believe no topics are off limits, however difficult this may feel. If you work with a skilled therapist they will be used to discussing sensitive issues and will find a way to nurture kindness and respect whilst acknowledging how you feel, as a couple or an individual.

Relational factors

It is important to consider how the relationship functions as a whole, especially if we think about the need for women to feel positive about their relationship as a precursor to nurturing desire.

The types of question I ask include:

- What is the relationship like in general?

- Do you feel you function well as an intimate team?

- Do you feel loved by your partner?

- You may love your partner, but do you actually like each other?

Sometimes a spouse will withhold sexual intimacy from their partner as a way to gain control in the relationship or to "punish" a partner. This may well be subconscious; perhaps the spouse is not even aware that they are holding on to unresolved anger.

Social issues

These are issues that are not directly related to sex but may indirectly affect the relationship. These may include factors that are affecting a couple's ability to have quality undisturbed and intimate time together, such as living with parents or in-laws, having small children, working unsocial hours, etc.

If I were meeting a couple in my practice where one spouse was presenting with absent or low sexual desire, I would want to get a detailed history from both parties. You might assume that a clinician would be more interested in the individual with the low desire, but actually what is usually more important is to look at what is going on within the couple's relationship. If we think about the concept of seasons of sex, we can fairly confidently assume that most of us will face challenges that may influence our sexual desire, but what is the key to getting through this as an intimate team? What do we need to understand about ourselves or our partner that would make navigating this together a possibility? How do we prevent ourselves becoming despondent or harbouring feelings of rejection which may cause distance rather than closeness in the marriage?

I work with a number of patients who have not had adequate sex education and do not feel confident in what they are doing sexually. This hinders their sexual enjoyment or may have created a pattern of unrealistic expectations about how they think they should "perform." Some patients describe situations where they are watching themselves, preoccupied with how they are performing, and this stops them being in the moment and enjoying the intimacy. This self-conscious watching is sometimes referred to as "spectatoring." If this is you then I would urge you to read Chapter 3 on expanding your sexual repertoire, to help you build confidence and enhance desire.

Precipitating (triggering) factors

When a couple starts to analyse their sexual relationship, they may realise there has always been a discrepancy in terms of their desires and needs. Or they may be able to identify a time when they did feel equally matched. This might have changed either suddenly or gradually. In either case, I would ask if the couple could identify things that happened in the run-up to the change – a trigger. This could be any number of scenarios, some of which have been identified earlier in the chapter in the section on biological factors, etc. This list is not exhaustive and there are any possible number of different things that can trigger a change in desire.

Maintaining factors

Maintaining factors can be the most important ones to consider in cases of low or absent sexual desire. This is primarily because, if we think about the concept of seasons of sex, recognising that sexual desire naturally ebbs and flows, then what is it about some couples that causes them to get stuck in winter?

If you are struggling, particularly if you recognise secondary desire issues (desire that was once there but has changed), it might be worth reminding yourself how you felt about your spouse when you were dating, on your wedding day, or on your honeymoon perhaps. Doing so might make it difficult for you to believe that you have moved so far apart and the intimate landscape of your marriage has changed so much. Or perhaps you realise desire has always been a problem for you. Do not give up hope, but as a couple commit to seeking help together, to search for what you have lost and hope to find again. You may even discover what you always hoped for but have not yet found.

God our Father, from the beginning, you have blessed creation with abundant life. Pour out your blessings upon this husband and this wife that they may be joined in mutual love and companionship.

Church of England marriage service

Female orgasmic disorder (FOD)

I have included female orgasmic disorder (FOD) here because many of the diagnostic criteria and treatment approaches for low desire/arousal disorder overlap those considered for female orgasmic disorder. Problems with orgasm can significantly affect how a person feels about sex: the more they worry about this, the less likely they are to become aroused and thus experience orgasm. It becomes a vicious cycle. I have covered issues with male orgasmic disorder in Chapter 10.

Female orgasmic disorder can be a lifelong problem (primary) or it might be an acquired problem (secondary). It might be a situational problem, i.e. the woman can achieve an orgasm when she stimulates herself but is unable to achieve an orgasm with her spouse.

FOD includes never having experienced an orgasm, infrequent orgasms, delayed orgasms, and a reduction in the strength of orgasmic sensations. They may also be painful. While some women do not need to have an orgasm to enjoy sex, having an orgasm is an important part of sexual satisfaction for others. Many feel under huge pressure to achieve an orgasm for the sake of their partner. A man can be very concerned that his wife does achieve an orgasm, to fulfil his expectations of being a good sexual partner himself. This can place more pressure on the woman, which can interrupt her arousal circuit, making it difficult for her to relax enough to be able to enjoy the sexual intimacy. The pressure to achieve orgasm then becomes a form of performance anxiety which makes orgasm less likely. Each time the woman has sexual contact, she worries she will not be able to achieve an orgasm, and so the pattern is repeated. Some women are able to feel very aroused but are then unable to orgasm. This can feel dissatisfying both physically and emotionally, and some women may also experience aching or discomfort in their pelvis and/or genital area.

Many women will need to feel relaxed enough to engage in enjoyable sexual contact sufficiently arousing to reach orgasm. Physical, emotional, and relationship factors can all affect this, as can adequate foreplay and feeling safe with their husband. Some women can experience orgasm on their own but not with their partner, as they feel too apprehensive about the vulnerability of "letting themselves go." Some find this hard to discuss with their partners, as they are not part of an intimate team. If this is the case for you, then a sex therapist might support you as a couple to discuss your feelings, or your partner's feelings, about your orgasmic experience, how important this is, and how you might address this as a couple.

Treatment for female orgasmic disorder

At present in the UK, no medication is approved specifically for treating orgasmic problems in women. Some self-help strategies can be useful, such as increasing the strength of your pelvic floor muscles. You can do exercises or you might need physiotherapy, and your GP can refer you on the NHS. You can also see physiotherapists privately, but check they have experience in this area, are fully qualified, and are registered with a recognised professional body, such as the Chartered Society of Physiotherapy (CSP).

Hormonal changes in oestrogen and/or testosterone could be

responsible for orgasmic problems, and they can be associated with the wider issue of low desire. HRT can help and is discussed later in the chapter. Medication can also cause problems, and your GP may be able to reduce the dose or switch the medication. If the issue is being caused by emotional or relationship problems, consider seeing a sex therapist. See Appendix 5 for more details. The book *Becoming Orgasmic* may also help.[1] It covers a range of issues but is focused on helping women to achieve orgasm.

Introducing a vibrator can reduce performance anxiety for both husband and wife, enabling the woman to get aroused much quicker than she might with manual or oral stimulation from her partner. It can also alleviate pressure on the husband to know how to arouse his wife sufficiently to achieve orgasm. Chapter 3 has more details, as does Appendix 3.

Who should seek help?

In Chapter 3, I raised the issue of couples falling back into sexual intimacy easily, when they are on holiday. This is a simple but useful question, because it can highlight what is happening. If a couple easily fall back into making love on holiday, then the issue of low desire is probably a logistics or planning issue, rather than a true diagnosis of low desire. The desire is there but is getting crowded out by other things. If you and your partner feel this is the case, then go back to Chapter 3 and implement some of the self-help strategies there. If you conclude that the problems are more complex than this, seek professional help.

Visiting your GP

Having read this chapter, you may have started to gain an understanding of what may have triggered your lack of desire/arousal and this information will be useful to your GP. You may have identified physical, psychological, or relational factors or a combination of any of these. You may also have identified predisposing, precipitating, and maintaining factors, and hopefully you will have a clearer understanding of whether the problems are situational or absolute, primary or secondary.

If you decide to seek help, then your first port of call should be your GP. You may then decide to see a sex therapist if it is agreed that there are no obvious physical causes for the low desire. You can find out more information in Chapter 5.

Hormone treatment for women

If your GP thinks you have reduced levels of the hormones oestrogen and testosterone, and tests confirm this, then you may benefit from hormone replacement therapy (HRT). Oestrogen levels fall in the perimenopausal phase and after the menopause. Oestrogen replacement can be given either systemically (to the whole body) or vaginally, to increase levels in this area only. Systemic oestrogen can be given by tablet, patch or skin gel. As well as positively improving libido it can also help other menopausal symptoms, such as hot flushes, vaginal dryness, and low mood. Vaginal oestrogens are inserted into the vagina and come in a tablet, ring or cream. Long-term treatment is needed, because symptoms will return if the treatment is stopped.

Testosterone in women is produced naturally in the ovaries and adrenal glands, and it is linked to female sexual function. A loss of sexual desire may be associated with a drop in testosterone levels. If a woman has her ovaries removed surgically, her levels of testosterone will suddenly fall.

In the UK, the only licensed testosterone treatment for many years was an implant put under the skin, using local anaesthetic. Testosterone gel and testosterone patches have also been used, but the patches have been withdrawn and the gel is not licensed for use in women. There has been some debate over the use of Flibanserin (Addyi™), a new drug for treating low sexual desire in women. It has to be taken every day and should not be combined with alcohol. It was approved for use in the United States in 2015, but has not yet been approved for use in the UK.

Women should always see their doctor before using this medication to ensure there are no health or medical concerns contributing to the symptoms. Some doctors are prepared to prescribe testosterone replacement drugs "off licence" in the UK because they are confident that the benefits outweigh the risks. In doing so they take on the responsibility for providing the patient with a drug that is not licensed for use. I would not advise taking this drug unless you are seeing a doctor who has specialised in this field, such as a gynaecologist or endocrinologist.

Hormone treatment for men

If the body is unable to make enough testosterone to work normally, this is called testosterone deficiency or hypogonadism. It can be primary, where the problem is in the testes, or secondary, where the problem is in the hypothalamus and pituitary gland. It can also be a combination of the two. Men are more likely to develop hypogonadism as they get older. Testosterone is the most important sex hormone in men. The body starts to produce testosterone during puberty, and it is essential for the development and maintenance of male characteristics. Testosterone also has effects on sexual function and on most major organs, including the brain, kidneys, bone, muscle, and skin.

Low testosterone levels increase a man's risk of developing cardiovascular disease (CVD), and as a result can increase his risk of early death. Low testosterone can also significantly reduce a man's quality of life. Testosterone production is controlled by both the brain and the testes. From the age of about thirty years, testosterone levels start to drop naturally. However, the production of testosterone does not usually stop altogether, and some men have higher levels than others as they age.

Older men are at increased risk of developing hypogonadism if they are obese or have other medical conditions such as metabolic syndrome, diabetes, and kidney disease, to name just a few. It is also more likely to occur if they have had testosterone suppressant therapy for prostate cancer, have prostate disease, have taken opiate drugs for a long time, or drink too much alcohol.

How is hypogonadism in men diagnosed?

Patients with hypogonadism may notice they have lost their night-time erections, experience erectile dysfunction (ED), or have low libido. They may also feel tired, depressed, or notice impaired concentration. Some men may notice they are losing muscle mass, becoming weaker, or gaining weight. Some men notice decreased body hair, gynaecomastia (breast development), or sleep disturbances. They may also experience hot flushes or sweats.

To make an accurate diagnosis and provide treatment, your doctor will consider your symptoms and will also check your testosterone levels. Men with ED, diabetes, and suspected hypogonadism should always have their testosterone checked, and usually this is best done before 9am when a man's testosterone peaks. You will need a blood test, and it will need to be repeated on another day to ensure an accurate reading.

Men who have erection problems, but do not respond very well to PDE5 inhibitors, should also have their testosterone checked. Erectile dysfunction drugs have been shown to be less effective in men whose testosterone levels are below the normal range.

If you are found to have low testosterone levels, you may be offered testosterone replacement therapy (TRT). There are various ways that this can be administered. It can be given as a gel which is rubbed into the skin every day, or as a long-acting injection which is given every six to twelve weeks, depending on how your testosterone levels respond to it.

TRT can provide a variety of benefits in men with hypogonadism. These include improvements in cardiovascular health, general mood, libido, and sexual function, as well as reduction in body fat and an increase in muscle mass. Such benefits are also likely to improve quality of life. However, TRT is also associated with some risks; your doctor should be able to discuss these with you. TRT may not be suitable for you if you have had prostate cancer. Once a man starts TRT, he should see his doctor for regular check-ups to make sure it is working well and not causing any problems. If he is not at increased risk of heart problems, and the testosterone level is stable, he should have regular blood tests every six to twelve months.

Conclusions

The topic of sexual desire is a complex one. Unlike the chapters on erectile dysfunction or vaginismus, I have sometimes struggled to convey all I have wanted to say, and at times this has left me a little despondent or overwhelmed. On some level I think this reflects what so many couples feel about issues of low sexual desire. They do not know why it feels such a struggle, but it does. They thought they would enjoy sex, but in practice it just feels like a hard slog. They struggle with something that should be natural, which everyone else seems to manage.

The issue of low sexual desire can be influenced by so many different factors, it is no wonder it can at times feel like a tightly wrapped knot, too difficult and perhaps too painful to unravel. I would encourage you not to become despondent, but slowly and steadily start to unpick the strands. Maybe you will need to read and reread this chapter and consider the different possible contributing factors. I hope, if nothing else, this chapter has been helpful in getting you thinking, and maybe you are already talking to your partner about what you think might be contributing to your desire issues. Perhaps you have already concluded that professional help would be helpful. It is worth investing the time and energy needed to help you as a couple move from a season of winter into warmer climates, or to protect the relationship from slipping into what you know could be a frosty season ahead. To avoid this, you must be determined to tackle the issues outlined in this chapter.

References

1. Julia R. Heiman and Joseph LoPiccolo, *Becoming Orgasmic*, (London: Piatkus, 1999).

Recommended reading

Gary Chapman, *The Five Love Languages*, (Chicago: Moody Press, 2015).

CONCLUSIONS

Till Death Us Do Part

Love is patient, love is kind. It does not envy, it does not boast,
it is not proud. It does not dishonour others, it is not self-seeking, it is not
easily angered, it keeps no record of wrong. Love does not delight in evil
but rejoices with the truth. It always protects, always trusts,
always hopes, always perseveres.

1 Corinthians 13:4–7

These verses are some of my favourite in the Bible, and they are among the most popular Bible verses to be read at traditional Christian wedding ceremonies. They tell us so much about human nature and that God speaks to us about the reality of love. Marriage has the potential to bring so much richness to our lives, through the depth and intimacy found in this unique bond. When we are basking in the sunshine during the sexual seasons of spring and summer, we might not ever imagine feeling jealous, being rude or chalking up wrongdoings, but how quickly those clouds can draw in. Suddenly, we feel our hearts hardened, remembering every little wrongdoing as we stand firm in the sense of our own righteousness. It is a comfort that this passage shows God knows the tensions and challenges that we face, not just in marriage, but in every human relationship.

If, as a couple, you are not currently facing challenges, that is wonderful. I hope you can use some of the strategies in this book to create an intimate team, ready to weather any future problems. If you are struggling, though, then I hope you now have the tools you need to get the right support, either through utilising the self-help strategies or through seeking professional help.

I also hope that the book has been able to dispel some of the widely held myths that sex is always spontaneous and effortlessly satisfying. Sex has seasons and we need to know how to manage these. As you will have read in Part I, there is much we can do to cultivate spring and summer to help our relationship flourish. However, it can be a challenge. We need to nurture erotic intelligence. We need to forget sexual spontaneity and embrace being intentional, which creates anticipation and fuels passion. We need enough distance to ensure we maintain and grow in our own identity; after all, this is what our spouse fell in love with when they met us.

We also need to understand how to develop true, authentic intimacy – not the kind that swamps our own or our partner's identity, but one that enables us to speak from a place of honesty and love. We need to remain playful, recognising that God created sexual intimacy to draw us together but also to have fun. He created a space for us to enjoy our and each other's bodies. Sometimes this will be passionate and exciting, sometimes enjoyable and predictable. Sometimes this might be just okay, and sometimes it might be a bit boring. Perhaps we are facing one of the problems covered in Part II of the book. Ultimately, though, if we draw together as an intimate team, all sexual intimacy can nurture love and closeness, and deepen our bond with our spouse.

In the same way that we need to dispel the world's view of sex, I think we also need to dispel some of the myths about love; that this should be easy, natural, and effortless. The Bible teaches us love has to be intentional. Love is listening to our spouse, and, to truly listen, we need to put aside our own desire to speak first, to make our case, to force our agenda. Love can be hard. Love has to endure, to remain firm when we feel we are not being heard, when we feel wronged or aggrieved.

Love also provides us with the ability to hope, and to believe that change is possible. Some couples find themselves so frost-bitten by the sexual season of winter they cannot imagine, or dare to hope for, something different. It's a bit like what the White Witch does in *The Lion, the Witch and the Wardrobe*. She turns the once lush green fields of Narnia into a perpetual state of winter.[1] Sometimes I work with couples who cannot see a way out. They feel they are so entrenched in a certain way of being together that they have lost all sense of hope that things can change.

If we are Christians, we need to remember that we cannot hope to live in our own strength. At times, we may feel so depleted and disheartened that we do not have the capacity to draw on any hope, and at this point we must turn to God. If you have turned to this book because you feel hopeless in your marriage, and unsure that things will ever change, then draw comfort from the promises that God makes to us:

'The LORD himself goes before you and will be with you; he will never leave you nor forsake you. Do not be afraid; do not be discouraged.'

Deuteronomy 31:8

'Have I not commanded you? Be strong and courageous. Do not be afraid; do not be discouraged, for the LORD your God will be with you wherever you go.'

Joshua 1:9

If you are not a Christian but you are interested in understanding more about the Christian faith then I would encourage you to attend an Alpha course. These are courses that are run all around the world and I have provided a link in Appendix 5 if you want to find out more. You may also like to consider attending The Marriage Course. This is a series of seven sessions, designed to help couples invest in their relationship and build a stronger marriage. It is based on Christian principles but is suitable for everyone, whether or not they are Christians. For more information please see Appendix 5.

I hope I have helped you to reframe the way that you might view sexual intimacy. If we choose to view sex as society does, then we are at risk of setting an unrealistically high bar and are likely to fall short. Then we may become critical – of ourselves and our partners – or may start making unhelpful comparisons.

So as I close I would like to say this. If you had come to my clinic, seeking help for a sexual problem, I would acknowledge this had taken courage. Sexual intimacy is complex, and rarely talked about in a way that enables people to be truly candid about what they are experiencing. This can make us feel we are different or inadequate in some way. But there are many options for couples to get help, which will enable them to enjoy a mutually satisfying and energised sexual life together, the warm climates of the spring and summer seasons of sex. Becoming an intimate team takes dedication, commitment, and regular re-evaluation, but it will ensure the frosts are kept at bay and the sexual season of winter has no chance to set in.

If you have chosen this book to look for ways to enhance your relationship, nurture intimacy or address a sexual difficulty, then you have also shown courage, and I commend you for that. I hope you too experience a renewed sense of faith, hope and love in your marriage.

And now these three remain: faith, hope and love. But the greatest of these is love.

1 Corinthians 13:13

References

1. C.S. Lewis, *The Lion, the Witch and the Wardrobe,* (London: HarperCollins, first published 1950; new edition 2009).

APPENDIX ONE

Erectile Dysfunction and
Prescribing Guidelines

Schedule 2 guidelines for prescribing restrictions for treatments for erectile dysfunction

There is a list of patients who are exceptions to the schedule 2 prescribing guidelines. These are men with one of the following conditions: diabetes, multiple sclerosis, Parkinson's disease, single gene neurological disease, prostate cancer, radical pelvic surgery, renal failure treated by dialysis, severe pelvic injury, spinal cord injury, spina bifida, poliomyelitis.

There are two additional categories: patients who were receiving ED drug treatment prior to 14 September 1998, and patients who are deemed to be suffering severe distress on account of their ED.

When the guidelines were originally introduced, patients who were requesting prescriptions under the severe distress clause were required to be seen in a specialist erectile dysfunction clinic for that decision to be endorsed. GPs now have the freedom to decide whether their patients meet the criteria for this, and there is some guidance for GPs about this.

It could be argued that most ED patients (by definition) suffer a marked effect on interpersonal relationships by being unable to have satisfactory sexual relationships, and therefore experience significant levels of stress.

The government guidelines also stipulate that, since their research showed couples on average had sex once a week, they recommended this as a guideline to GPs. For some couples this may be adequate, but for others one tablet a week would not be enough. However, it is up to the prescribing clinician to decide what each couple needs, in discussion with their patients.

Second-line treatments

There are two types of Alprostadil injections available: Caverject® and Viridal®. Invicorp (aviptadil and phentolamine mesilate) is another type of injection therapy used to treat ED. These drugs are injected directly into the spongy tissue of the penis and a spontaneous erection occurs within about ten to fifteen minutes, lasting about half an hour. Caution has to be taken if you are using any blood-thinning drugs such as Warfarin.

Another second-line treatment is the use of intra-urethral pellets. Alprostadil (MUSE®) is a small pellet that is inserted into the urethra (the tube through which you pass urine). The pellet dissolves and is absorbed into the spongy tissue of the penis, giving a spontaneous erection.

Both these two above treatments may rarely cause priapism: an erection that lasts more than four hours. This is considered to be a serious medical emergency. Before penile injection treatment is prescribed, your GP or specialist would take a detailed medical history and give you all the relevant information you need to commence treatment, including what to do in the event of a priapism. You would also be shown in the clinic how to give yourself an injection.

Other second-line treatments are:

Topical cream: Alprostadil (Vitaros®) is a cream that is applied to the opening (meatus) of the penis and the surrounding skin with a special applicator.

Vacuum pump devices: A vacuum pump device draws blood into the penis under negative pressure and is trapped in the penis using a constriction ring at the base of the penis. This does not sound appealing to many patients, but in my experience, it can be very effective, particularly for couples who have been married for some time and are comfortable with each other sexually.

There are many pumps available. I have experienced working with a company called imedicare. More information about their pumps can be found at: www.imedicare.co.uk

Penile implant surgery: This is seen as a last resort treatment when all other treatments have failed. Surgically implanted devices (penile prostheses) are inserted in place of the corpus cavernosal tissue in the penis. These implants are either inflatable or malleable rods. The inflatable rods are connected to a fluid-filled bag that sits in the scrotal sac. When the man wants to have an erection, he manipulates a trigger button underneath the skin of the scrotum and this releases the fluid into the rods which then inflate. The button then deflates the rods and draws the fluid back into the reservoir bag. The malleable rods can be directed up for an erection and then pushed down when an erection is no longer required.

Testosterone replacement: Testosterone replacement therapy may be required if you are found to have low levels of this hormone. This can be particularly relevant if you are not responding to the PDE5i tablet treatments. As part of your assessment your GP will check your testosterone levels by taking a blood sample.

Pelvic floor exercises: Research has suggested that a small number of men with ED may benefit from exercises to strengthen the pelvic floor muscles. These muscles lie underneath the bladder and back passage, and at the base of the penis. If your doctor thinks this approach may benefit you, they will refer you to a physiotherapist.

APPENDIX TWO

Early Ejaculation and Peyronie's Disease

Peyronie's disease

Peyronie's disease is the formation of tough, fibrous plaques within the penis that can be felt initially as painful lumps. The flaccid penis usually appears unaffected but when the penis becomes erect, it inflates unevenly and tends to bend around the plaque, causing the appearance of Peyronie's disease. Some men are barely troubled by it, while others find sexual intercourse physically impossible, and it can also contribute to ED. It is thought that Peyronie's disease affects about 3–9 percent of all adult men.[1]

In mild cases men will not require treatment, but all men who suspect they may have Peyronie's disease should seek medical help to prevent the condition from getting worse. There are a number of treatment options available for Peyronie's in addition to the treatments we have discussed for ED.

References

1. Pryor, J.P., Ralph, D.J. (2002) Clinical presentations of Peyronie's disease. *International Journal of Impotence Research* 14, 414–17.

APPENDIX THREE

Vaginal Dilators, Vibrators and Lubricants

Some vaginal dilators and lubricants are available on prescription from your GP. This may vary between surgeries, depending on local budget contracts, so you would need to discuss it with them. There are also a number of different vaginal dilators and lubricants available to buy, without a prescription. Deciding which one you choose will be personal preference.

A very user-friendly online shop that sells a variety of vaginal dilators and an extensive array of vaginal lubricants is called *Stress No More*. They sell a large range of dilators and lubricants from different manufacturers. More information can be found at:
www.stressnomore.co.uk, 01482 496 931

Sh! Women's Emporium is another good shop based in Hoxton. They also have an online shop. Sh! promotes sexual enjoyment by women for women. All the staff are female and are trained to work with women and couples experiencing difficulties. The shop also runs a number of educational workshops, including one for women suffering with vaginismus and you can read more about these on the shop's website. As a man you can go to the shop, but only at designated times of the week and only if you are accompanying a female partner. Sh! sells a wide range of vibrators, dilators, and vaginal lubricants. More information can be found at: www.sh-womenstore.com, 0333 344 4005

There are lots of good vaginal lubricants on the market but one I regularly recommend is a brand called *Yes*. These are a range of organic lubricants and can be purchased through the outlets I have listed above, through Amazon or directly from: www.yesyesyes.org

For more information on pelvic floor exercises, see: www.nhs.uk/common-health-questions/womens-health/what-are-pelvic-floor-exercises

APPENDIX FOUR

Mindfulness

Mindfulness is increasingly being used in therapy and more generally as a way to help people manage stress and anxiety. You can read more about this approach on the NHS website:
www.nhs.uk/conditions/stress-anxiety-depression/pages/mindfulness

You can also find out more information on mindfulness at:
www.mentalhealth.org.uk

This is a UK-based charity which looks at all aspects of mental health and well-being. This website gives more information on the practice of mindfulness, lists practitioners in your area, and advertises nationwide courses.

APPENDIX FIVE

Useful Organisations

ORGANISATION	AIM	CONTACT DETAILS
Alpha International	Alpha is a series of sessions helping people explore the principles of the Christian faith.	www.alpha.org
The Marriage Course	The Marriage Course is a series of seven sessions, designed to help couples invest in their relationship and build a strong marriage.	www.themarriage courses.org
Relate	A UK-based charity aiming to help people develop and support healthy relationships. Relate offer individual or couple counselling at centres located all over the UK.	www.relate.org.uk

The College of Sex and Relationship Therapists (COSRT)	A UK-based charity to support healthy, satisfying and rewarding personal relationships. COSRT provides practical suggestions and advice for people who feel their personal relationships might need some help. It provides a list of UK sex and relationship therapists.	www.cosrt.org.uk 0208 543 2707
UK Council for Psychotherapy (UKCP)	An organisation for the education, training, accreditation, and regulation of psychotherapists and psychotherapeutic counsellors in the UK. Provides listings of accredited psychotherapists.	www.psychotherapy.org.uk 0207 014 9955
British Association for Counselling and Psychotherapy (BACP)	Promotes expertise in the counselling professions and provides a list of accredited counsellors and psychotherapists in the UK.	www.bacp.co.uk 0145 588 3300
National Counselling Society (NCS)	Supports and promotes counselling and counsellors in the UK and provides a list of accredited therapists.	www.nationalcounsellingsociety.org 0190 320 0666

The Samaritans	Provides counselling and support on any issue of concern.	www.samaritans.org 116123
UK Association of Transactional Analysis (UKATA)	Professional body for people interested in and practising Transactional Analysis (TA) within the UK. Provides a list of counsellors, psychotherapists, organisational consultants, and educators who are trained in TA.	www.uktransactional analysis.co.uk 0189 266 4615
Family Planning Association (FPA)	Sexual health charity providing information on sexual and reproductive health.	www.fpa.org.uk 0845 122 8690
The Vulval Pain Society	A UK registered charity supporting vulval pain sufferers.	www.vulvalpainsociety. org
NHS General Health information	The website provides information about all aspects of health.	www.nhs.uk/pages/ home.aspx
NHS Sexual Health	The website provides information about sexual health and allows you to search for your nearest sexual health service.	www.nhs.uk/livewell/ sexualhealth

Female Genitial Mutilation: NHS information and support for victims	Information and support for victims of female genital mutilation.	www.nhs.uk/ conditions/female-genital-mutilation
Safeline	A specialised charity working to prevent sexual abuse and to support those affected in their recovery. This includes working with people whose mental health issues suggest that they may be vulnerable to abuse.	www.safeline.org.uk 0192 640 2498
Rape Crisis	Provide advice and support if you have experienced rape, child sexual abuse, and/or any kind of sexual violence. They can provide details of your nearest Rape Crisis services and information for friends, partners, family and other people supporting a sexual violence survivor.	**England and Wales:** www.rapecrisis.org.uk 0808 802 9999 **Scotland:** www.rapecrisis scotland.org.uk 0808 801 0302 **Northern Ireland 24 hour Domestic and Sexual Violence helpline:** 0808 802 1414

Men's Advice Line	Provides advice and support for men in abusive relationships.	www.mensadviceline.org.uk 0808 801 0327
The Association for the Treatment of Sexual Addiction and Compulsivity (ATSAC)	Provides information and support on sex addiction and compulsivity for addicts and their partners.	www.atsac.co.uk 0741 478 7341
The Marylebone Centre	A clinic that offers treatment, support, and professional therapeutic training in sex addiction.	www.marylebonecentre.co.uk 0203 322 4147
The Laurel Centre	The Laurel Centre is a specialist organisation providing sexual addiction therapy. The centre also provides support for partners and sex addiction training to counsellors. The Laurel Centre was founded by Paula Hall & Associates who are the UK's largest provider of sex addiction and porn addiction therapy services.	info@thelaurelcentre.co.uk **Leamington Spa:** First Floor 50-54 Regent Street Royal Leamington Spa Warwickshire CV32 5EG 0192 633 9594 **London:** 76 Cleveland Street London W1T 6ND 0207 965 7302

Covenant Eyes Internet Accountability and Filtering	Covenant Eyes services are designed to help you overcome pornography by monitoring your online activity and sending a report to a trusted friend who holds you accountable for your online choices.	www.covenanteyes.com
Sex Addicts Anonymous	A twelve-step recovery programme for sex addicts.	www.saauk.info 0784 310 8302 0759 991 7686
Co-dependents of Sex Addicts (COSA)	A twelve-step recovery programme for men and women whose lives have been affected by another person's compulsive sexual behaviour	www.cosa-recovery.org

This list is in no way exhaustive and there will be many other organisations who can offer you additional support and advice.

I have no financial interests in any of the organisations or products I discuss in this book.

22790453R00138

Printed in Great Britain
by Amazon